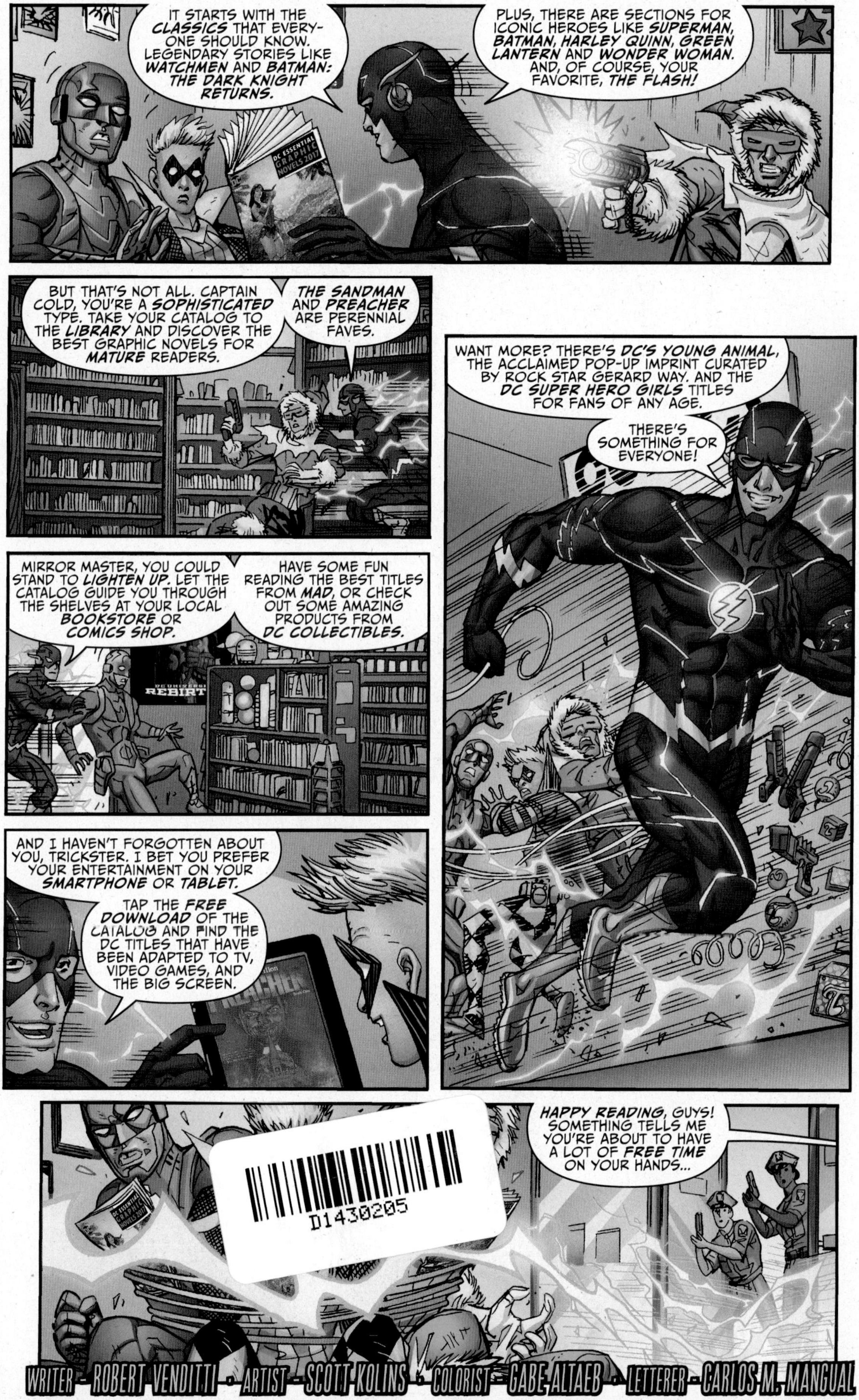

IT STARTS WITH THE CLASSICS THAT EVERY-ONE SHOULD KNOW. LEGENDARY STORIES LIKE WATCHMEN AND BATMAN: THE DARK KNIGHT RETURNS.
DC ESSENTIAL GRAPHIC NOVELS 2017
PLUS, THERE ARE SECTIONS FOR ICONIC HEROES LIKE SUPERMAN, BATMAN, HARLEY QUINN, GREEN LANTERN AND WONDER WOMAN. AND, OF COURSE, YOUR FAVORITE, THE FLASH!
BUT THAT'S NOT ALL. CAPTAIN COLD, YOU'RE A SOPHISTICATED TYPE. TAKE YOUR CATALOG TO THE LIBRARY AND DISCOVER THE BEST GRAPHIC NOVELS FOR MATURE READERS.
THE SANDMAN AND PREACHER ARE PERENNIAL FAVES.
MIRROR MASTER, YOU COULD STAND TO LIGHTEN UP. LET THE CATALOG GUIDE YOU THROUGH THE SHELVES AT YOUR LOCAL BOOKSTORE OR COMICS SHOP.
HAVE SOME FUN READING THE BEST TITLES FROM MAD, OR CHECK OUT SOME AMAZING PRODUCTS FROM DC COLLECTIBLES.
REBIRTH
AND I HAVEN'T FORGOTTEN ABOUT YOU, TRICKSTER. I BET YOU PREFER YOUR ENTERTAINMENT ON YOUR SMARTPHONE OR TABLET.
TAP THE FREE DOWNLOAD OF THE CATALOG AND FIND THE DC TITLES THAT HAVE BEEN ADAPTED TO TV, VIDEO GAMES, AND THE BIG SCREEN.
PREACHER
WANT MORE? THERE'S DC'S YOUNG ANIMAL, THE ACCLAIMED POP-UP IMPRINT CURATED BY ROCK STAR GERARD WAY. AND THE DC SUPER HERO GIRLS TITLES FOR FANS OF ANY AGE.
THERE'S SOMETHING FOR EVERYONE!
DC ESSENTIAL GRAPHIC NOVELS 2017
HAPPY READING, GUYS! SOMETHING TELLS ME YOU'RE ABOUT TO HAVE A LOT OF FREE TIME ON YOUR HANDS...

WRITER - ROBERT VENDITTI • ARTIST - SCOTT KOLINS • COLORIST - GABE ALTAEB • LETTERER - CARLOS M. MANGUAL

DC ESSENTIAL GRAPHIC NOVELS 2017.

Cover art by Tony S. Daniel
Intro story by Robert Venditti, Scott Kolins and Gabe Eltaeb

2900 West Alameda Ave., Burbank, CA
Printed by Transcontinental Interglobe, Beauceville, QC, Canada. 11/18/2016.
ISBN: 978-1-4012-7328-6

Table of Contents

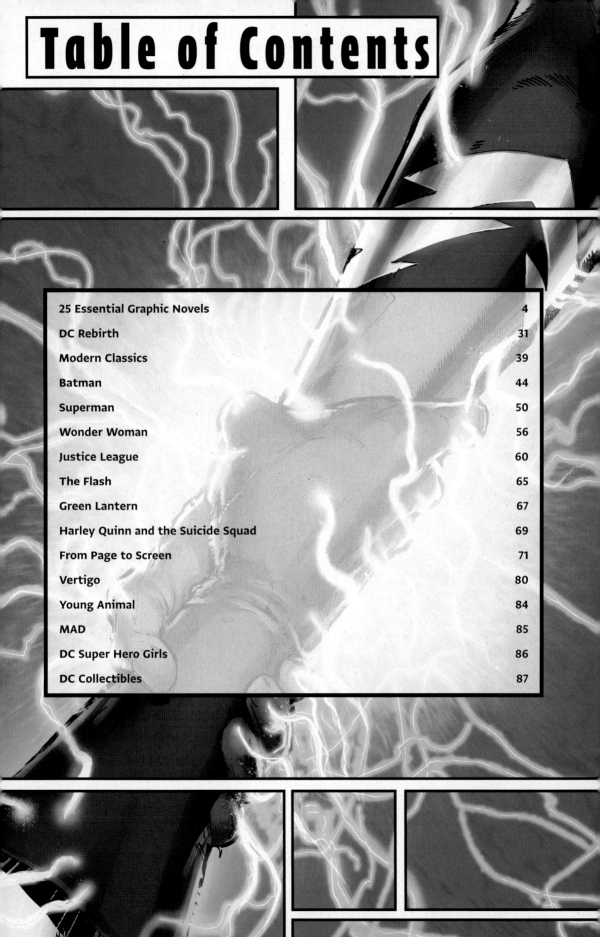

25
ESSENTIAL
CLIFF
CHIANG
2011

GRAPHIC NOVELS

WATCHMEN

THE GREATEST GRAPHIC NOVEL OF ALL TIME

One of the most influential graphic novels of all time and a perennial bestseller, WATCHMEN is considered a gateway title to the entire graphic storytelling medium. Alan Moore and Dave Gibbons' seminal story is the benchmark against which all other graphic novels and comic books are judged.

A murder mystery turned nationwide conspiracy, WATCHMEN examines the lives of the eponymous superhero team as they seem to decay alongside the ever-darkening America around them. Rorschach, Nite Owl, the Silk Spectre, Dr. Manhattan and Ozymandias reunite to investigate who's behind a teammate's murder, but find that the truth may be even more grim than the world they seek to protect.

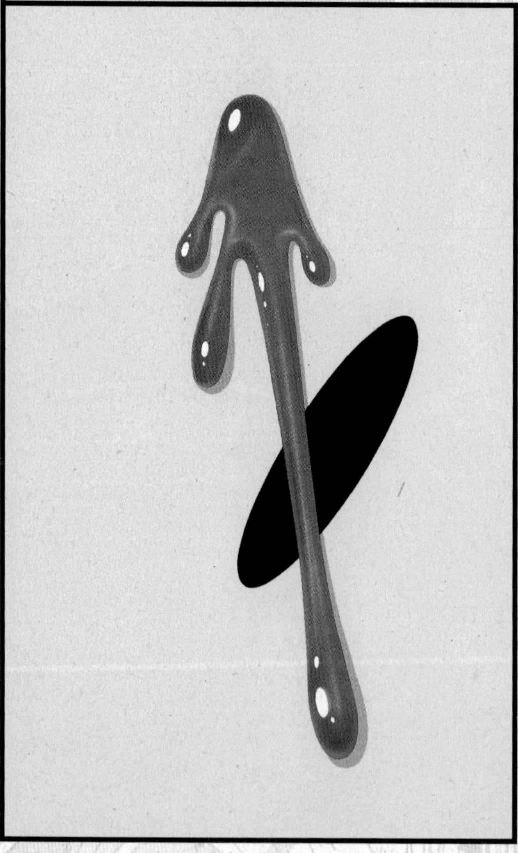

"A WORK OF RUTHLESS PSYCHOLOGICAL REALISM, IT'S A LANDMARK IN THE GRAPHIC NOVEL MEDIUM. IT WOULD BE A MASTERPIECE IN ANY."
–*TIME*, *TIME'S* 100 BEST ENGLISH-LANGUAGE NOVELS FROM 1923 TO THE PRESENT

"REMARKABLE. THE WOULD-BE HEROES OF **WATCHMEN** HAVE STAGGERINGLY COMPLEX PSYCHOLOGICAL PROFILES."
– *THE NEW YORK TIMES BOOK REVIEW*

"DARK, VIOLENT AND BLACKLY FUNNY, **WATCHMEN** IS A COMIC BOOK LIKE NO OTHER. [IT IS] THE *CRIME AND PUNISHMENT* OF GRAPHIC NOVELS."
–*LONDON TIMES*

WATCHMEN

Writer: Alan Moore | Artist: Dave Gibbons | ISBN: 978-1-4012-4525-2 | Diamond Code: FEB140265 | Price: $19.99 US/$23.99 CAN | Format: TP

BATMAN: THE KILLING JOKE

ALAN MOORE'S UNFORGETTABLE MEDITATION ON THE RAZOR-THIN LINE BETWEEN SANITY AND INSANITY, HEROISM AND VILLAINY, COMEDY AND TRAGEDY

In this groundbreaking work, Moore weaves together a twisted tale of insanity and human perseverance featuring Batman's greatest foe, the Joker.

Looking to prove that any man can be pushed past his breaking point into madness, the Joker attempts to drive Commissioner Gordon insane. Refusing to give up even after suffering a tremendous personal tragedy, Gordon struggles to maintain his sanity with the help of Batman in a desperate effort to best the madman.

With art by Brian Bolland, one of comics' best illustrators, BATMAN: THE KILLING JOKE remains DC's best-selling graphic novel more than 25 years after its inception.

"EASILY THE GREATEST JOKER STORY EVER TOLD, **BATMAN: THE KILLING JOKE** IS ALSO ONE OF ALAN MOORE'S FINEST WORKS. IF YOU'VE READ IT BEFORE, GO BACK AND READ IT AGAIN. YOU OWE IT TO YOURSELF." –IGN

"I LOVED THE KILLING JOKE. IT'S MY FAVORITE. IT'S THE FIRST COMIC I EVER LOVED." –TIM BURTON

"A GENUINELY CHILLING PORTRAYAL OF BATMAN'S GREATEST FOE." –BOOKLIST

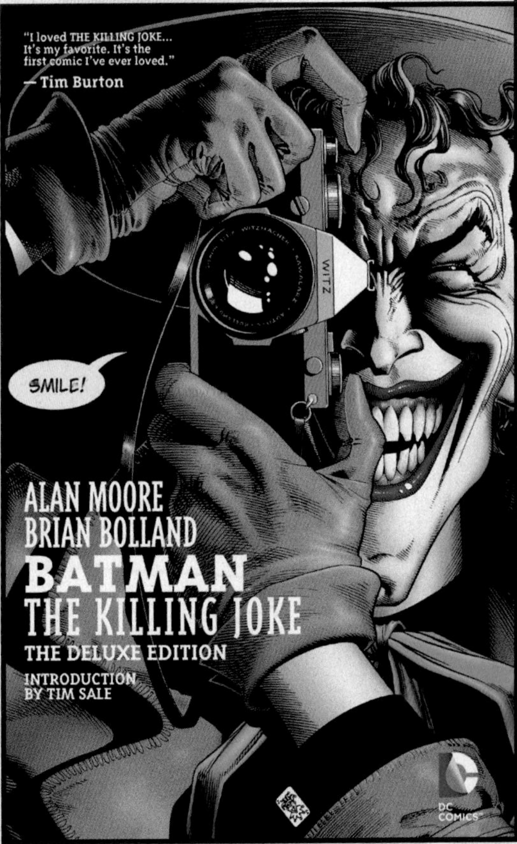

BATMAN: THE KILLING JOKE

Writer: Alan Moore | Artist: Brian Bolland | ISBN: 978-1-4012-1667-2 | Diamond Code: NOV150279 | Price: $17.99/$20.99 CAN | Format: HC

FOR MATURE READERS

BATMAN: THE DARK KNIGHT RETURNS

FRANK MILLER'S INFLUENTIAL GRAPHIC NOVEL JUGGERNAUT THAT ALTERED THE PERCEPTION OF THE GENRE

"GROUNDBREAKING." –USA TODAY

"CHANGED THE COURSE OF COMICS." –ROLLING STONE

"REVISIONIST POP EPIC." –SPIN

"IT'S FILM NOIR IN CARTOON PANELS." –VANITY FAIR

Ten years after an aging Batman has retired, Gotham City has sunk deeper into decadence and lawlessness. Now, when his city needs him most, the Dark Knight returns in a blaze of glory. Joined by Carrie Kelley, a teenage female Robin, Batman must take back the streets.

But for a man his age, a return to a life of crime-fighting is not easy. After facing off against two of his greatest enemies, the Joker and Two-Face, a haggard Batman finds himself in mortal combat with his former ally, Superman, in a battle that only one of them will survive.

Hailed as a comics masterpiece, THE DARK KNIGHT RETURNS is Frank Miller's (*300* and *Sin City*) reinvention of Gotham's legendary protector. It remains one of the most influential stories ever told in comics, with its echoes felt in all media forms of DC storytelling.

BATMAN: THE DARK KNIGHT RETURNS

Writer: Frank Miller | Artist: Frank Miller | ISBN: 978-1-4012-6311-9 | Diamond Code: NOV118095 | Price: $19.99/$23.99 CAN | Format: TP

THE SANDMAN VOL. 1: PRELUDES & NOCTURNES

THE DEFINITIVE VERTIGO SERIES BY THE LEGENDARY NEIL GAIMAN

The *New York Times* best-selling author Neil Gaiman's transcendent series THE SANDMAN is often labeled as not only the definitive Vertigo title, but also as one of the finest achievements in graphic storytelling.

In THE SANDMAN VOLUME 1: PRELUDES & NOCTURNES, an occultist attempting to capture Death to bargain for eternal life traps her younger brother Dream instead. After his seventy-year imprisonment and eventual escape, Dream, also known as Morpheus, goes on a quest for his lost objects of power to reclaim his reign.

Gaiman, a celebrated storyteller and award-winning creator the world over, has forged an incredible legacy with this groundbreaking saga, the ripples of which are still felt today.

"THE SANDMAN JUST MIGHT BE THE SMARTEST COMIC BOOK EVER WRITTEN." –USA TODAY

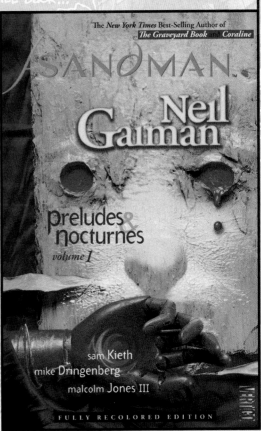

"NEIL GAIMAN'S LONG-RUNNING SERIES MADE COOL COMICS FANTASTICAL AND FANTASTICAL COMICS COOL. **THE SANDMAN** IS A MODERN MYTH, AS WELL AS A PRÉCIS ON WHY THE STORIES WE TELL MATTER SO MUCH." –PLAYBOY

"THE GREATEST EPIC IN THE HISTORY OF COMIC BOOKS." –LOS ANGELES TIMES MAGAZINE

THE SANDMAN VOL. 1: PRELUDES & NOCTURNES

Writer: Neil Gaiman | Artists: Sam Kieth, Malcolm Jones III & Mike Dringenberg | ISBN: 978-1-4012-2575-9 | Diamond Code: JUL100259

Price: $19.99/$23.99 CAN | Format: TP | FOR MATURE READERS

BATMAN
VOL. 1: THE COURT OF OWLS

"[WRITER SCOTT SNYDER] PULLS FROM THE OLDEST ASPECTS OF THE BATMAN MYTH, COMBINES IT WITH SINISTER COMIC ELEMENTS FROM THE SERIES' BEST PERIOD AND GIVES THE WHOLE THING A TERRIFIC FORWARD-SPIN BY SETTING UP AN HONEST-TO-GOSH MYSTERY FOR BATMAN TO SOLVE."
–*ENTERTAINMENT WEEKLY*

A NEW ERA FOR THE DARK KNIGHT AND GOTHAM CITY BEGINS HERE IN THIS #1 *NEW YORK TIMES* BESTSELLER!

"SNYDER MIGHT BE THE DEFINING BATMAN WRITER OF OUR GENERATION."
–*COMPLEX MAGAZINE*

Batman has heard tales of Gotham City's Court of Owls: that the members of this powerful cabal are the true rulers of Gotham. The Dark Knight dismissed the stories as rumors and old wives' tales. Gotham was his city. Until now.

A brutal assassin is sinking his razor-sharp talons into the city's best and brightest, as well as its most dangerous and deadly. If the dark legends are true, his masters are more powerful predators than the Batman could ever imagine.

With every year that passes, Scott Snyder and Greg Capullo's masterpiece becomes more entrenched in this medium's pantheon of the greatest stories ever told.

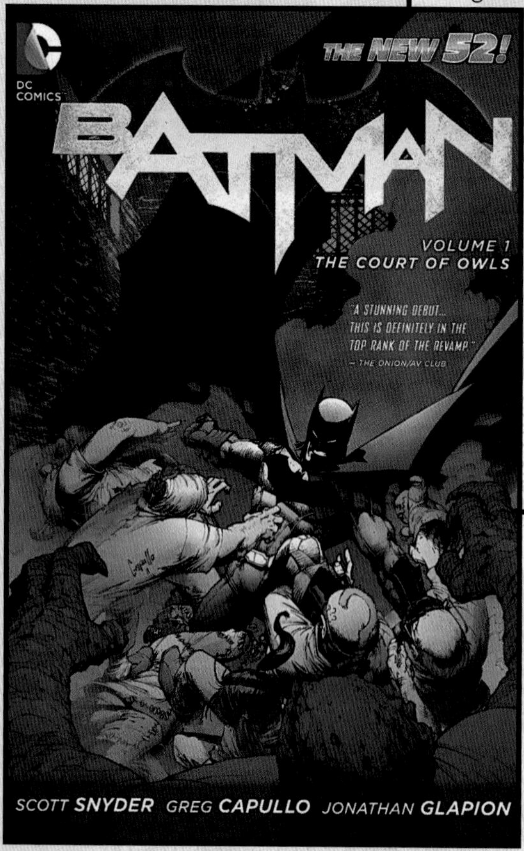

"A STUNNING DEBUT...SNYDER KNOWS THESE CHARACTERS, SETS UP AN INTRIGUING MYSTERY AND DELIVERS SOME ACTION THAT CAPULLO REALIZES STUNNINGLY. THIS IS DEFINITELY IN THE TOP RANK OF THE REVAMP." –A.V. CLUB/THE ONION

BATMAN VOL. 1: THE COURT OF OWLS

Writer: Scott Snyder | Artist: Greg Capullo | ISBN: 978-1-4012-3542-0 | Diamond Code: DEC120323 | Price: $16.99/$19.99 CAN | Format: TP

V FOR VENDETTA

A DARK PORTRAIT OF OPPRESSION AND RESISTANCE SET AGAINST THE BACKDROP OF DYSTOPIAN FUTURE ENGLAND

"DARK, GRIPPING STORYTELLING."
–ENTERTAINMENT WEEKLY

A visionary graphic novel that defines sophisticated storytelling, Alan Moore's best-selling V FOR VENDETTA is a terrifying portrait of totalitarianism and resistance, superbly illustrated by artist David Lloyd.

Set in a futuristic totalitarian England, a country without freedom or faith, a mysterious man in a white porcelain mask strikes back against the oppressive overlords on behalf of the voiceless. This powerful story detailing the loss and fight for individuality has become a cultural touchstone and an enduring allegory for current events.

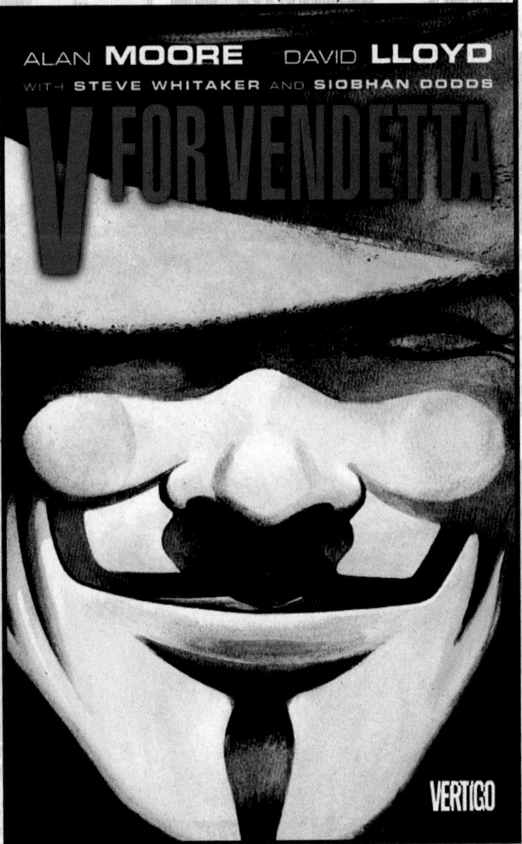

"DENSELYPACKED, THEMATICALLY VIBRANT AND PHILOSOPHICALLY CHALLENGING."
SCRIPPS HOWARD NEWS SERVICE

V FOR VENDETTA

Writer: Alan Moore | Artist: David Lloyd | ISBN: 978-1-4012-0841-7 | Diamond Code: SEP088030 | Price: $19.99/$23.99 CAN | Format: TP

FOR MATURE READERS

JUSTICE LEAGUE

VOL. 1: ORIGIN

"A MUST-READ."
–COMPLEX MAGAZINE

GEOFF JOHNS AND JIM LEE UNITE FOR THE FIRST TIME TO LAUNCH THE BOLD NEW BEGINNING OF THE DC UNIVERSE'S PREMIER SUPER HERO TEAM!

Two of the greatest titans of the comics industry come together to tell the definitive story featuring the World's Greatest Super Heroes in JUSTICE LEAGUE VOL. 1: ORIGIN.

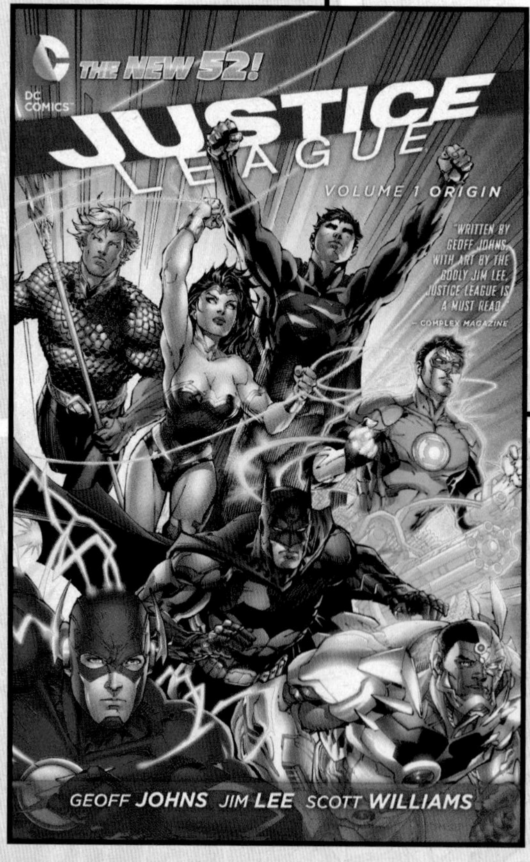

It's the dawn of a new age of superheroes, frightening to the world at large. Superman. Batman. The Flash. Wonder Woman. Green Lantern. Aquaman. Cyborg. Though young and inexperienced, brash and overconfident, each one alone is a powerful force in the battle of good against evil. Together, they may be the only thing on Earth that can stop the alien warlord Darkseid from claiming our planet as his own. Together they will become the Justice League!

"WELCOMING TO NEW FANS LOOKING TO GET INTO SUPERHERO COMICS FOR THE FIRST TIME AND OLD FANS WHO GAVE UP ON THE FUNNY BOOKS LONG AGO."
–*MTV GEEK*

"WRITER GEOFF JOHNS AND ARTIST JIM LEE TOSS YOU–AND THEIR HEROES–INTO THE ACTION FROM THE VERY START AND DON'T PUT ON THE BRAKES. DC'S ÜBER-CREATIVE TEAM CRAFT AN INVITING WORLD FOR THOSE WHO ARE TRYING OUT A COMIC FOR THE FIRST TIME." –*USA TODAY*

JUSTICE LEAGUE VOL. 1: ORIGIN

Writer: Geoff Johns | Artist: Jim Lee | ISBN: 978-1-4012-3788-2 | Diamond Code: OCT120252 | Price: $16.99/$19.99 CAN | Format: TP

BATMAN: HUSH

IN ONE OF THE MOST ACCESSIBLE GRAPHIC NOVELS EVER WRITTEN, SUPERSTAR CREATORS JEPH LOEB AND JIM LEE DIG DEEP INTO THE DARK KNIGHT'S ROGUES' GALLERY FOR THIS EPIC ADVENTURE

"THE REAL STAR, THOUGH, IS JIM LEE'S ART, WHICH JUST MIGHT BE HIS BEST WORK IN HIS TIME AT DC COMICS." –IGN

Gotham City's worst criminals have emerged to throw Batman's life into utter chaos. However, these villains—Joker, Riddler, Ra's al Ghul, Clayface and others—are part of a much more elaborate, sinister scheme to destroy the Dark Knight once and for all. Pushed past his breaking point, Batman will need to use more than the world's greatest detective skills to uncover the true mastermind behind this murderous plot before those closest to Bruce Wayne suffer the consequences.

In this truly unforgettable story by two of comics' top talents, writer Jeph Loeb and DC Co-Publisher Jim Lee present the Caped Crusader's most personal case yet.

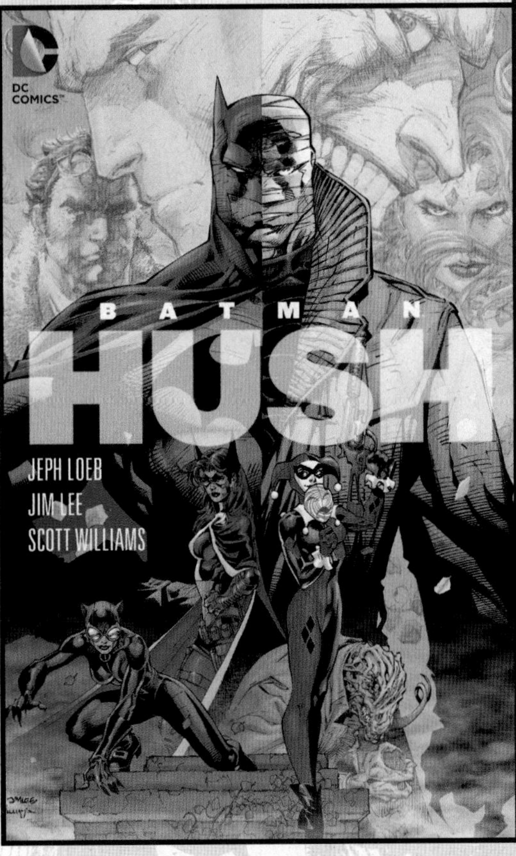

"IT'S BEAUTIFUL STUFF. CATWOMAN HAS RARELY LOOKED SO SEDUCTIVE, NOR HAS BATMAN'S HEROIC BUT FEARSOME IMAGE OFTEN BEEN USED SO WELL. [HUSH] MAKE[S] READERS LOOK AT BATMAN AND HIS COLLEAGUES WITH A FRESH, ENTHUSIASTIC EYE." –PUBLISHERS WEEKLY

BATMAN: HUSH

Writer: Jeph Loeb | Artist: Jim Lee | ISBN: 978-1-4012-2317-5 | Diamond Code: MAY090178 | Price: $24.99/$29.99 CAN | Format: TP

ALL-STAR SUPERMAN

THE CRITICALLY ACCLAIMED, GENRE-BENDING SERIES THAT HARKENS BACK TO THE GOLDEN AGE OF SUPERMAN

"MANIACALLY BRILLIANT." –THE NEW YORK TIMES

The Underverse ruled by Bizarros. The time-eating Chronovore. Jimmy Olsen, Super Hero?

Nothing is impossible in ALL-STAR SUPERMAN.

The unstoppable creative team of writer Grant Morrison and artist Frank Quitely join forces once more to take Superman back to basics. In an emotionally and visually stunning graphic novel harkening back to a Golden Age of comics, ALL-STAR SUPERMAN creates a new, and at the same time familiar, take on the world's first superhero.

"A STIRRINGLY MYTHIC, EMOTIONALLY RESONANT, AND GLORIOUSLY ALTERNATIVE TAKE ON THE MAN OF STEEL." –ENTERTAINMENT WEEKLY

"TAKING THE MAN OF STEEL BACK TO HIS ROOTS AND INTO THE FUTURE AT THE SAME TIME, ALL-STAR SUPERMAN IS EXCITING, BOLD AND SUPERCOOL…ALL THE MAKINGS OF A CLASSIC." –VARIETY

ALL-STAR SUPERMAN

Writer: Grant Morrison | Artist: Frank Quitely | ISBN: 978-1-4012-3205-4 | Diamond Code: JUL110247 | Price: $29.99/$35.00 CAN | Format: TP

PREACHER
BOOK ONE

"FEATURES MORE BLOOD AND BLASPHEMY THAN ANY MAINSTREAM COMIC IN MEMORY. COOL."
–*ENTERTAINMENT WEEKLY*

"THE MOST INTENSE ADULT COMIC IN AGES."
–*SPIN*

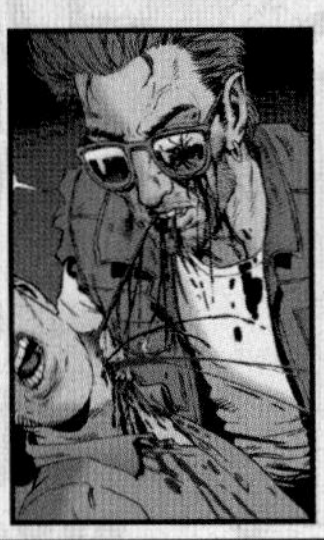

IN THIS HEARTFELT AND UNAPOLOGETICALLY PROFANE GRAPHIC NOVEL THAT INSPIRED THE TV SERIES, *PREACHER* FOLLOWS THE EPIC JOURNEY OF REVEREND JESSE CUSTER AS HE TRACKS DOWN A FUGITIVE GOD

Jesse Custer was just a small-town preacher in Texas, trying to help his fellow man, until his congregation was flattened by powers beyond his control.

Now possessed by Genesis—the unholy coupling of an angel and demon—Jesse holds Word of God, an ability to command anyone or anything with a mere utterance. And he'll use this power to hold the Lord accountable for the people He has forsaken.

From the ashes of a small-town church to the bright lights of New York City to the backwoods of Louisiana, Jesse Custer cuts a righteous path across the soul of America in his quest for the divine—an effort that will be met by every evil that Heaven and Earth can assemble. Joined by his gun-toting girlfriend, Tulip, and the hard-drinking Irish vampire, Cassidy, Jesse will stop at nothing to fulfill his quest to find God.

Garth Ennis and Steve Dillon bring readers on a violent and riotous journey across the country in this award-winning Vertigo series.

"IT WILL RESTORE YOUR FAITH IN COMICS."
–*NEW YORK DAILY NEWS*

"JUST ABOUT THE BEST THING TO COME ALONG SINCE COMICS STARTED FINDING THEIR WAY INTO BOOKS."
–*WASHINGTON POST*

PREACHER BOOK ONE

Writer: Garth Ennis | Artist: Steve Dillon | ISBN: 978-1-4012-4045-5 | Diamond Code: MAR130303 | Price: $19.99/$23.99 CAN | Format: TP

FOR MATURE READERS

BATMAN:
YEAR ONE

THE TIMELESS ORIGIN STORY OF THE DARK KNIGHT

"IT'S NOT ONLY ONE OF THE MOST IMPORTANT COMICS EVER WRITTEN, IT'S ALSO AMONG THE BEST." –IGN

In 1986, Frank Miller and David Mazzucchelli produced this groundbreaking reinterpretation of the origin of Batman—who he is, and how he came to be. Sometimes careless and naive, this Dark Knight is far from the flawless vigilante he is today. In his first year on the job, Batman feels his way around a Gotham City far darker than the one he left. His solemn vow to extinguish the town's criminal element is only half the battle; along with Lieutenant James Gordon, the Dark Knight must also fight a police force more corrupt than the scum in the streets.

BATMAN: YEAR ONE stands next to BATMAN: THE DARK KNIGHT RETURNS as one of the greatest Batman graphic novels of all time. Timeless in its appeal, Frank Miller and David Mazzucchelli's masterpiece would stand out in the crowded comics field even today.

"THERE'S NEVER BEEN STORYTELLING QUITE LIKE THIS. IT TOOK SOMEONE WHO VIEWS COMICS AS AN ART TO CREATE IT." –*WASHINGTON POST*

"THIS IS A STORY NO TRUE BATMAN FAN SHOULD BE ABLE TO RESIST." –*SCHOOL LIBRARY JOURNAL*

BATMAN: YEAR ONE

Writer: Frank Miller | Artist: David Mazzucchelli | ISBN: 978-1-4012-0752-6 | Diamond Code: OCT060163 | Price: $14.99/$17.99 CAN | Format: TP

WONDER WOMAN VOL. 1: BLOOD

CRITICALLY ACCLAIMED WRITER BRIAN AZZARELLO TEAMS WITH CLIFF CHIANG AND TONY AKINS TO CREATE A NEW WONDER WOMAN MYTHOLOGY

Experience a bold new beginning of the iconic character in WONDER WOMAN VOLUME 1: BLOOD—a critically acclaimed and best-selling series!

Wonder Woman's world is shattered when a secret her mother, Hippolyta, queen of the Amazons, kept all her life is revealed: Diana is not clay brought to life, but is in fact the child of Zeus! In this reimagining of Diana's history, superheroics and mythology seamlessly blend as Brian Azzarello (JOKER, 100 BULLETS) creates a new direction for one of the world's best-known heroes. With stunning art by Cliff Chiang and Tony Akins, Wonder Woman has never looked better.

"BEAUTIFULLY ILLUSTRATED AND BRINGS A FRESH, FASCINATING AND FUN TAKE TO THE AMAZON PRINCESS AND HER WORLD." –IGN

"AZZARELLO IS...REBUILDING THE MYTHOLOGY OF WONDER WOMAN." –*MAXIM*

"IT'S A DIFFERENT DIRECTION FOR WONDER WOMAN, BUT ONE STILL STEEPED IN MYTHOLOGY...GREAT THINGS FROM AZZARELLO AND CHIANG."
–*A.V. CLUB/THE ONION*

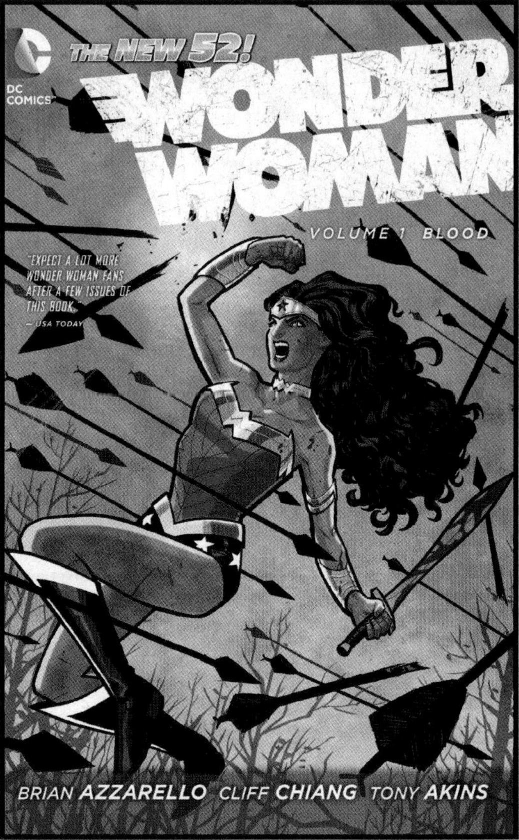

WONDER WOMAN VOLUME 1: BLOOD

Writer: Brian Azzarello | Artists: Cliff Chiang & Tony Akins | ISBN: 978-1-4012-3562-8 | Diamond Code: OCT120256
Price: $14.99/$17.99 CAN | Format: TP

DC: THE NEW FRONTIER

THIS EISNER, HARVEY AND SHUSTER AWARD-WINNING SERIES TAKES READERS ON AN EPIC JOURNEY FROM THE END OF THE GOLDEN AGE OF HEROES TO THE BEGINNINGS OF THE LEGENDARY JUSTICE LEAGUE OF AMERICA.

"THE CARTOONIST DARWYN COOKE IS AN EXTRAORDINARY TALENT… [NEW FRONTIER] IS AN AUDACIOUS REVISIONIST LOOK AT THE FORMATION OF THE JUSTICE LEAGUE." –*THE NEW YORK TIMES*

Welcome to 1950s America—a land of promise and paranoia, of glittering cities and segregated slums, of dizzying scientific progress and simmering Cold War conflict. A land where super heroes have been outlawed. Those icons who do still fight on—Superman, Wonder Woman, Batman—must operate under hidden agendas and dueling ideologies.

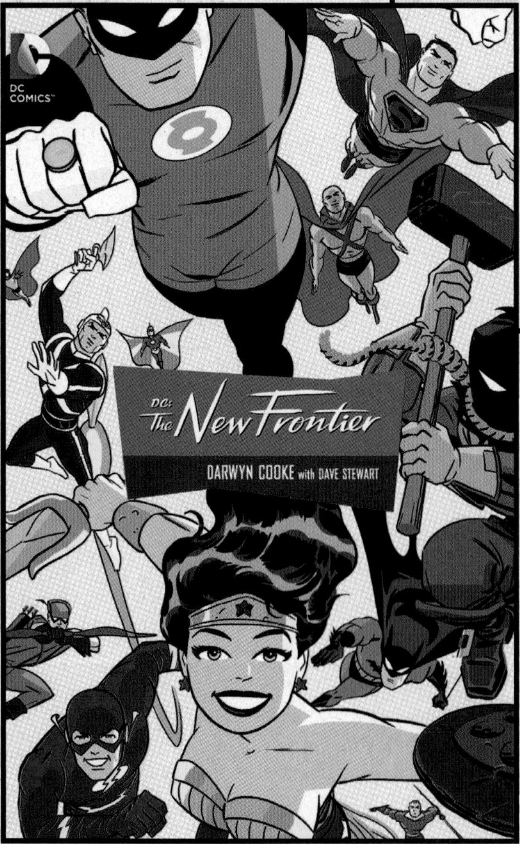

One of the greatest talents in the history of the medium, the inimitable Darwyn Cooke, takes the helm as he seamlessly intertwines superhero icons with American history to create a rich tapestry of timeless storytelling. DC: THE NEW FRONTIER is emotionally complex, heart-stopping and simply astounding.

"COOKE HAS STIRRINGLY LAID OUT A PROMISING NEW PATH FOR THE SUPERHERO GENRE." –*PUBLISHERS WEEKLY*

"USING A CLASSIC STYLE, COOKE CREATES A CLASSIC OF HIS OWN…" –*A.V. CLUB/THE ONION*

DC: THE NEW FRONTIER

Writer: Darwyn Cooke | Artist: Darwyn Cooke | ISBN: 978-1-4012-4888-8 | Diamond Code: OCT140355 | Price: $34.99/$41.99CAN | Format: HC

BATMAN: EARTH ONE

GEOFF JOHNS REIMAGINES THE DARK KNIGHT'S ORIGIN STORY IN THIS GRAPHIC NOVEL THAT BEGS TO BE READ IN ONE SITTING

Batman is not a hero. He is just a man. Fallible, vulnerable and angry.

In Gotham City, where friend and foe are indistinguishable, Bruce Wayne's path toward becoming the Dark Knight is riddled with more obstacles than ever before. Focused on punishing his parents' true killers, and the corrupt police who allowed them to go free, Bruce Wayne's thirst for vengeance fuels his mad crusade and no one, not even Alfred, can stop him.

In this #1 *New York Times* bestseller, writer Geoff Johns and artist Gary Frank reimagine a new mythology for the Dark Knight, where the familiar is no longer the expected, in this original graphic novel.

"JUST WHEN YOU THOUGHT THERE COULDN'T POSSIBLY BE A FRESH TAKE ON BATMAN, ALONG COME JOHNS AND FRANK TO PROVE YOU EXTRAORDINARILY WRONG. ORIGINAL, SURPRISING AND EMOTIONAL, **BATMAN: EARTH ONE** IS A MUST-READ." –DAMON LINDELOF (CO-CREATOR AND EXECUTIVE PRODUCER OF LOST)

"THIS ISN'T JUST ABOUT CAPES AND TIGHTS. THIS IS STUFF THAT, LIKE THE BEST OF FICTION, GOES BEYOND THE PARAMETERS OF ITS PARTICULAR GENRE." –MTV GEEK

"GEOFF JOHNS, THE CHIEF CREATIVE OFFICER AT DC COMICS, HAS WRITTEN US A BATMAN FOR EARTH ONE THAT WILL KNOCK YOUR SOCKS OFF." –HUFFINGTON POST

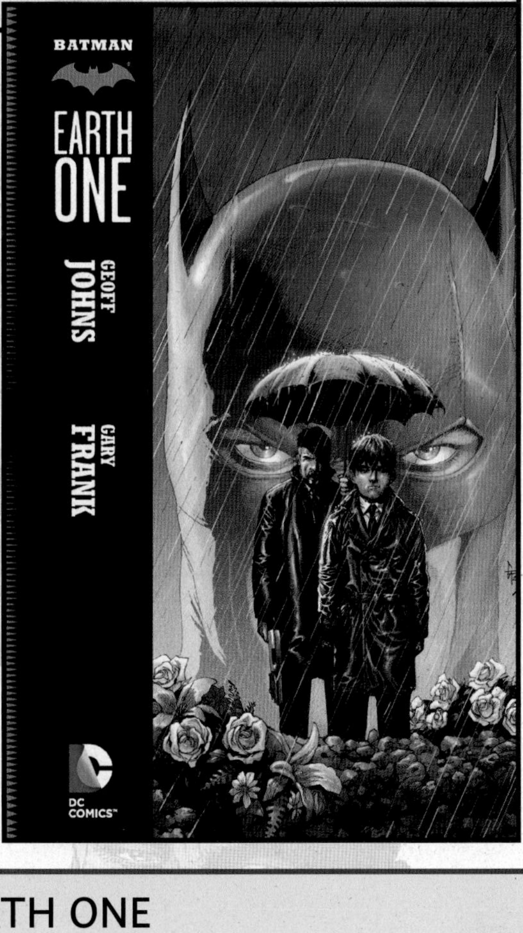

BATMAN: EARTH ONE

Writer: Geoff Johns | Artist: Gary Frank | ISBN: 978-1-4012-3209-2 | Diamond Code: JUL158202 | Price: $14.99/$17.99 CAN | Format: TP

DC UNIVERSE: REBIRTH
THE DELUXE EDITION

THE COURSE OF THE DC UNIVERSE IS CHANGED FOREVER IN THIS HEARTFELT TALE OF LOVE, LOSS AND HOPE, ALL LEADING UP TO ONE OF THE MOST SHOCKING ENDINGS IN COMICS HISTORY

From Crisis to Zero Hour, to a Flashpoint in time, to a New 52 universe, nothing has affected the World's Greatest Super Heroes as much as the threat that's careening toward them. Meanwhile, a mysterious force ripples across the cosmos, trying to warn them of this impending doom. That force? A returning Wally West.

This graphic novel brings together the incredible legacy of DC, with decades of mythology colliding with new characters and adventures, all launching us into a new era of vivid storytelling called DC Rebirth.

Written by Geoff Johns and illustrated by four of the industry's best artists—Gary Frank, Ivan Reis, Ethan Van Sciver and Phil Jimenez—this graphic novel shatters all the unwritten rules in comics and, from those pieces, creates an all-new status quo for the DC Universe.

"GEOFF JOHNS IS INJECTING HEART AND HUMANITY BACK INTO THE LIVES AND ADVENTURES OF DC COMICS' ICONIC SUPERHEROES." –*USA TODAY*

"DELIVERS A JAW-DROPPING TWIST THAT WILL HAVE IMPLICATIONS FOR YEARS TO COME." –*YAHOO! MOVIES*

"A COMPASS FOR THE NEW ERA." –*WALL STREET JOURNAL*

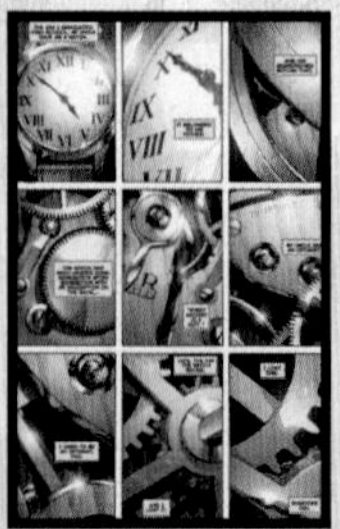

DC UNIVERSE: REBIRTH THE DELUXE EDITION

Writer: Geoff Johns | Artists: Gary Frank, Ivan Reis, Ethan Van Sciver and Phil Jimenez | ISBN: 978-1-4012-7072-8 | Diamond Code: AUG160316

Price: $17.99/23.99 CAN | Format: HC

BATMAN: THE LONG HALLOWEEN

A CLASSIC BATMAN MURDER MYSTERY BY THE ICONIC CREATIVE TEAM OF JEPH LOEB AND TIM SALE

Set just after Batman's first year in Gotham City, the Dark Knight finds himself working alongside District Attorney Harvey Dent and Lieutenant James Gordon, trying to vanquish the criminal element. However, a serial killer known only as Holiday has been killing friendS and foeS each month. Batman races against the calendar trying to discover the assassin's identity, fighting the entirety of Gotham's rogues' gallery along the way.

The magnificent creative team of Jeph Loeb and Tim Sale reach their apex in BATMAN: THE LONG HALLOWEEN, propelling the graphic novel to its place among comics' finest murder-mystery stories.

"THE LONG HALLOWEEN STRETCHES BEYOND THE NORMAL BOUNDARIES OF COMICS TO CREATE A LEGENDARY STORY OF ONE MAN'S CRUSADE AGAINST AN INSANE WORLD." –IGN

"THE LONG HALLOWEEN IS MORE THAN A COMIC BOOK. IT'S AN EPIC TRAGEDY." –CHRISTOPHER NOLAN (DIRECTOR OF BATMAN BEGINS, THE DARK KNIGHT AND THE DARK KNIGHT RISES)

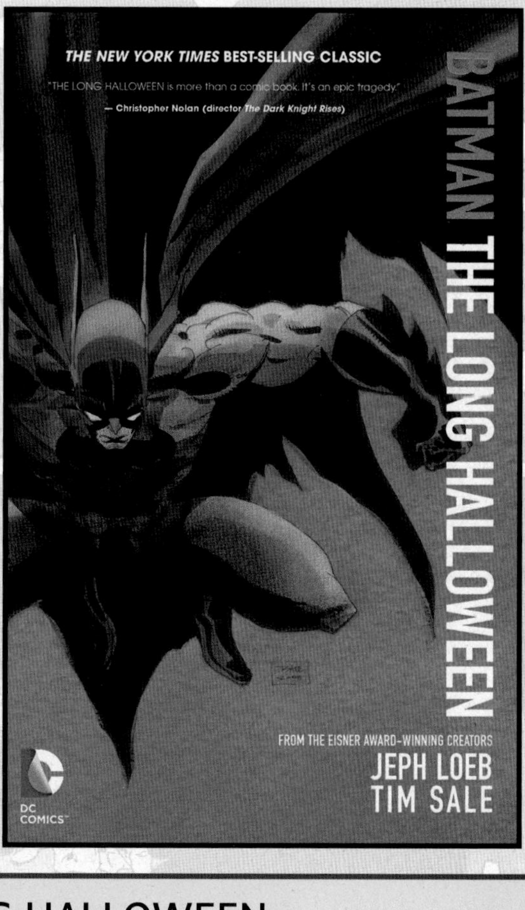

BATMAN: THE LONG HALLOWEEN

Writer: Jeph Loeb | Artist: Tim Sale | ISBN: 978-1-4012-3259-7 | Diamond Code: JUL110251 | Price: $24.99/$28.99 CAN | Format: TP

THE FLASH
VOL. 1: MOVE FORWARD

"THE FLASH IS SIMPLY COMICS AT ITS FINEST." –POPMATTERS

A BOLD NEW VISION OF THE SCARLET SPEEDSTER, BREATHTAKINGLY RENDERED BY ONE OF COMICS' BEST ARTISTS

Struck by a bolt of lightning and doused in chemicals, Central City police scientist Barry Allen was transformed into the Fastest Man Alive. But there are some things even the Flash can't outrun. Trying since his youth to solve his mother's murder, Barry has often ignored what was in front of his very eyes. And that personal grudge might end up affecting the Flash just as much as his alter ego.

Written and gorgeously illustrated by the creative tag team of Francis Manapul and Brian Buccellato, THE FLASH VOL. 1: MOVE FORWARD is the perfect vision of the Scarlet Speedster brought to life. This stunning graphic novel is one of the fastest and easiest entry points in all of DC Comics' vast library.

"A VISUAL TREAT...ANY READER CAN EASILY JUMP ON BOARD." –THE NEW YORK TIMES

"THIS IS WHY COMIC BOOKS ARE AWESOME." –CRAVEONLINE

THE FLASH VOL. 1: MOVE FORWARD

Writers: Francis Manapul & Brian Buccellato | Artist: Francis Manapul | ISBN: 978-1-4012-3554-3 | Diamond Code: MAY130224

Price: $16.99/$19.99 CAN | Format: TP

BATGIRL VOL. 1: BATGIRL OF BURNSIDE

THE TRAILBLAZING CREATIVE TEAM OF CAMERON STEWART, BRENDEN FLETCHER AND BABS TARR REINVENT BATGIRL FOR A NEW GENERATION

Smart, savvy, chic and resourceful, Barbara Gordon is ready for a fresh start. That's exactly what the classic character gets—a new look, a new crew of friends and a fresh voice—in this vibrant and unexpected series overhaul. But when Batgirl starts trending as Gotham's first viral vigilante, she also attracts a new wave of enemies looking to steal her social media spotlight.

Cameron Stewart, Brenden Fletcher and Babs Tarr revolutionize one of the most iconic female superheroes of all time in this incredibly relatable, socially relevant graphic novel that brings Batgirl to life more than any previous interpretation.

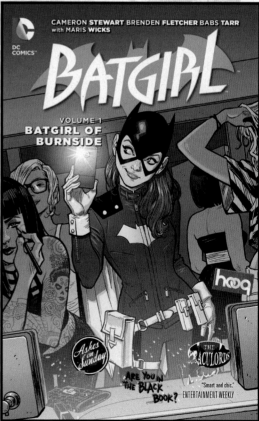

"THE BATGIRL TITLE AT DC HAS MAYBE NEVER BEEN BETTER, UNDER THE CREATIVE TEAM OF CAMERON STEWART, BRENDEN FLETCHER AND BABS TARR." –NERDIST

"THIS IS A MUST-BUY SERIES." –THE NEW YORK TIMES

"THIS REINVIGORATION OF BATGIRL MANAGES TO BE BIG FUN AND ACTUALLY TUNED IN TO MILLENNIAL CULTURE... THOROUGHLY ENJOYABLE. SURE TO PLEASE SUPERHERO FANS OF ALL AGES." –SCHOOL LIBRARY JOURNAL

BATGIRL VOL. 1: BATGIRL OF BURNSIDE

Writers: Brenden Fletcher & Cameron Stewart | Artist: Babs Tarr | ISBN: 978-1-4012-5798-9| Diamond Code: DEC148636

Price: $14.99/$17.99 CAN | Format: TP

INJUSTICE:
GODS AMONG US YEAR ONE—
THE COMPLETE COLLECTION

"STARTS OFF WITH A BANG."
-FORBES

THE #1 *NEW YORK TIMES* BEST-SELLING PREQUEL TO THE SMASH HIT VIDEO GAME

You've played the game, but you don't know the whole story. Forget everything you think you know about the Man of Steel. Tradition is tossed aside and chaos erupts as Superman struggles to shoulder blame for the death of Lois Lane and their unborn child. Undone by grief and rage, he abandons his renowned moral code in favor of an unforgiving brand of justice.

As Superman's staunchest allies are divided by his stark transformation, conflicting visions of a new world order soon arise—and the looming crisis threatens to ignite when Batman emerges as his most vocal challenger.

In this epic prelude to the smash-hit video game phenomenon, INJUSTICE: GODS AMONG US YEAR ONE—THE COMPLETE EDITION pits two longtime allies—Batman and Superman—against each other as the DC Universe is torn in half!

"AN ENTERTAINING GATEWAY INTO THE NEW GAME UNIVERSE." -IGN

INJUSTICE: GODS AMONG US YEAR ONE—THE COMPLETE COLLECTION

Writer: Tom Taylor | Artists: Jheremy Raapack & Mike S. Miller| ISBN: 978-1-4012-6279-2 | Diamond Code: DEC150338

Price: $24.99/29.99 CAN| Format: TP

FABLES VOL. 1: LEGENDS IN EXILE

FOLKLORE COMES TO LIFE AS THESE REAL-LIFE FAIRY-TALE CHARACTERS ARE EXILED IN MODERN-DAY NEW YORK CITY

"[A] WONDERFULLY TWISTED CONCEPT." –*WASHINGTON POST*

Writer and creator Bill Willingham has created a new world for these beloved fables...one that exists within our own.

When a savage creature known only as the Adversary conquered the homeland of legends and myth, all of the infamous inhabitants of folklore were forced into exile. Disguised among the normal citizens of modern-day New York, these magical characters created their own secret society called Fabletown. But when Snow White's party-girl sister, Rose Red, is apparently murdered, it is up to Bigby, the reformed Big Bad Wolf and Fabletown's sheriff, to find the killer.

FABLES VOLUME 1: LEGENDS IN EXILE is the critically acclaimed, best-selling first chapter of one of Vertigo's great staple series.

"AN EPIC, BEAUTIFULLY WRITTEN STORY." –THE ONION

"GREAT FUN." –*BOOKLIST*

FABLES VOL. 1: LEGENDS IN EXILE

Writer: Bill Willingham | Artist: Lan Medina | ISBN: 978-1-4012-3755-4 | Diamond Code: FEB120285 | Price: $12.99/$15.99 | Format: TP

FOR MATURE READERS

FLASHPOINT

THE COURSE OF COMICS WAS FOREVER CHANGED IN THIS GRAPHIC NOVEL THAT SET THE STAGE FOR A NEW ERA IN THE DC UNIVERSE

WAYNE

In a world where Wonder Woman and Aquaman have plunged millions into war, where no human has ever wielded the Green Lantern's light and no one has heard of Superman, Barry Allen—a.k.a. The Flash—is the only man who remembers the world as it should be. How can the Fastest Man Alive bring his reality back? And what price will he pay?

This action-packed adventure is a creative tour de force by two titans of the medium, Geoff Johns and Andy Kubert, as they plunge the Scarlet Speedster into an epic battle, the ramifications of which can still be felt in today's comics. FLASHPOINT isn't just one of this generation's most heart-pounding stories, it's also one of its most important.

"Heroic comic-book art at its finest" - ENTERTAINMENT WEEKLY / SHELF LIFE
GEOFF JOHNS · ANDY KUBERT · SANDRA HOPE
FLASHPOINT
"A soaring, if radical, tale that uses superheroes in ways that may surprise both first-time readers and long-time fans." – THE ASSOCIATED PRESS
DC COMICS

"HEROIC COMIC-BOOK ART AT ITS FINEST."
–*ENTERTAINMENT WEEKLY/ SHELF LIFE*

"AMBITIOUS." –*USA TODAY*

"A SOARING, IF RADICAL, TALE THAT USES SUPERHEROES IN WAYS THAT MAY SURPRISE BOTH FIRST-TIME READERS AND LONGTIME FANS."
–ASSOCIATED PRESS

FLASHPOINT

Writer: Geoff Johns | Artist: Andy Kubert | ISBN: 978-1-4012-3338-9 | Diamond Code: OCT138324 | Price: $16.99/$19.99 CAN | Format: TP

THE SANDMAN: OVERTURE

THE WIDELY ACCLAIMED, MUST-READ PREQUEL TO NEIL GAIMAN'S LEGENDARY SANDMAN SERIES

Twenty-five years after THE SANDMAN changed the landscape of modern comics, Neil Gaiman returns to his monumental series and answers lingering questions about the origins of Morpheus and his siblings: Death, Desire, Despair, Delirium, Destruction and Destiny. All of it leads up to the events of THE SANDMAN VOL. 1: PRELUDES AND NOCTURNES, in which Dream has been imprisoned for decades.

Accompanied by breathtaking artwork by J.H. Williams III that stretches the boundaries of what is possible on the comic page, this newest chapter in THE SANDMAN library is an essential addition to any casual or serious collector's bookshelves.

"A SWEEPING AND EXTRAVAGANT PREQUEL." -ENTERTAINMENT WEEKLY

"THIS UNTOLD TALE DOESN'T FEEL AS MUCH LIKE A DISTANT SATELLITE AS AN UNDISCOVERED CONTINENT TO THE SANDMAN MYTH, BRIMMING WITH THE SAME OTHER-WORLDLY DELIGHT THAT GAIMAN REVELS IN."
-*PASTE MAGAZINE*

"AS WEIRD AND MAGICICAL AND DREAMY AS EVER." -*TIME*

THE SANDMAN: OVERTURE

Writer: Neil Gaiman | Artist: J.H. Williams III | ISBN: 978-1-4012-6519-9 | Diamond Code: AUG160359 | Price: $19.99/$25.99 CAN | Format: TP

GOTHAM ACADEMY

VOL. 1: WELCOME TO GOTHAM ACADEMY

THE INNOVATIVE CREATIVE TEAM OF BECKY CLOONAN, BRENDEN FLETCHER AND KARL KERSCHL EXPLORE THE FRINGES OF BATMAN'S TOWN IN THIS COMING-OF-AGE TALE OF TWO YOUNG GIRLS AT A GOTHAM CITY PREP SCHOOL

Gotham Academy isn't like other schools. But Olive Silverlock isn't like other students. After a mysterious incident over summer break, she's back at school with a bad case of amnesia, an even worse attitude...and an unexplained fear of bats.

Olive's supposed to show new student Maps Mizoguchi the ropes. Problem: Maps is the kid sister of Kyle, Olive's ex. Then there's the ghost haunting the campus...the secret society conducting bizarre rituals...and Bruce Wayne, the weirdo billionaire who funds the Academy—and who may know the secret to Olive's big mystery.

Accessible to readers young and old, GOTHAM ACADEMY VOL. 1: WELCOME TO GOTHAM ACADEMY is a revelation of mythmaking that sets it apart from anything else in the DC library.

"A LITTLE BIT CW TELEVISION SERIES AND A LITTLE BIT HARRY POTTER, WITH A WEE TOUCH OF MANGA-INSPIRED STORYTELLING...A REALLY FUN AND CHARMING BOOK." –NERDIST

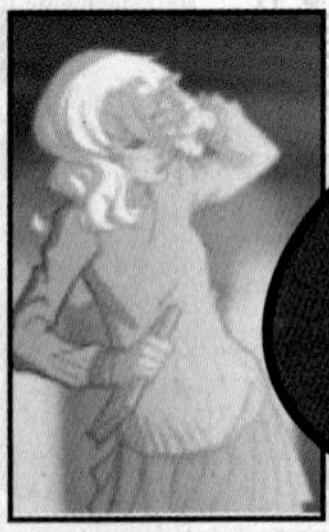

"SLICK, CHARMING, AND, DARE WE SAY IT, FUN." –IGN

"AS IT TURNS OUT, IT'S SPOOKY, WEIRD AND LIKE NOTHING DC COMICS HAS EVER RELEASED BEFORE." –MTV NEWS

GOTHAM ACADEMY VOL. 1: WELCOME TO GOTHAM ACADEMY

Writers: Becky Cloonan & Brenden Fletcher | Artist: Karl Kerschl | ISBN: 978-1-4012-5472-8 | Diamond Code: MAR150269

Price: $14.99/$17.99 CAN| Format: TP

WONDER WOMAN: EARTH ONE VOL. 1

MIND-BENDING SCRIBE GRANT MORRISON ONCE AGAIN WORKS HIS ALCHEMY ON ANOTHER OF DC'S ICONIC HEROES, CREATING THE MOST PROVOCATIVE ORIGIN OF WONDER WOMAN YOU'VE EVER SEEN

For millennia, the Amazons of Paradise Island have created a thriving society away from the blight of man. One resident, however, is not satisfied with this secluded life—Diana, Princess of the Amazons, knows there is more in this world and wants to explore, only to be frustrated by her protective mother, Hippolyta.

Diana finds her escape when Air Force pilot Steve Trevor, the first man she has ever seen, crashes onto their shores. With his life hanging in the balance, Diana must venture into the long-forbidden world of men.

Thought-provoking yet reverent, thoroughly modern but still timeless, the power and courage of Paradise Island's greatest champion—Wonder Woman—is introduced by the masterful minds of Grant Morrison and Yanick Paquette (SWAMP THING, BATMAN, INC.). This new addition to DC's *New York Times* best-selling Earth One original graphic novel series is a wholly unique retelling of the Amazon Warrior's origin.

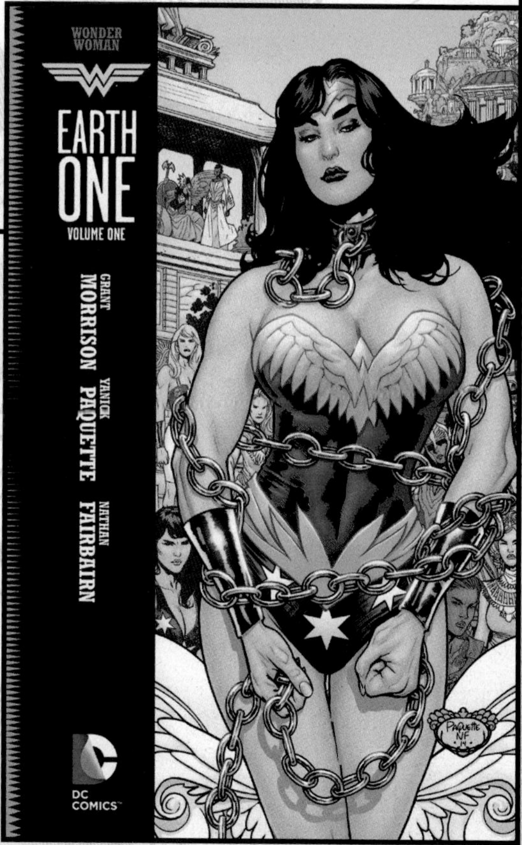

"MORRISON OFFERS A FIERCER, STRANGER, MORE EPIC, MORE TEXTURED, AND, INCIDENTALLY, MORE DIVERSE INTERPRETATION." -*BOOKLIST*

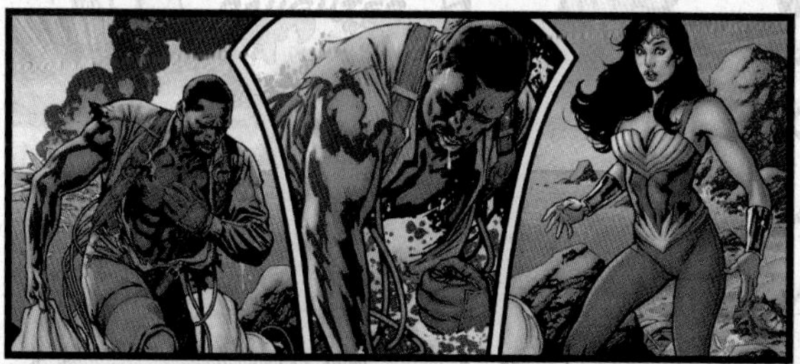

"YANICK PAQUETTE'S ART CELEBRATES THE CLEAR CONFIDENCE OF DIANA AND THE AMAZONS, THEIR POSTURE IMMACULATELY PROUD AND NATURAL." -*PASTE MAGAZINE*

WONDER WOMAN: EARTH ONE VOL. 1

Writer: Grant Morrison | Artist: Yanick Paquette | ISBN: 978-1-4012-6863-3 | Price: $16.99/$22.99 CAN | Format: TP

AQUAMAN
VOL. 1: THE TRENCH

LEGENDARY CREATIVE DUO GEOFF JOHNS AND IVAN REIS RETEAM TO LAUNCH THE KING OF ATLANTIS BACK INTO PROMINENCE

Aquaman is back to challenge his status as a second-tier Super Hero. Maligned for years as the man who talks to fish, Arthur Curry stakes his claim as one of the most powerful heroes in the DC Universe in AQUAMAN VOL. 1: THE TRENCH. As the King of the Seven Seas, Aquaman has sworn to protect his ocean home, and there's been no greater threat to date than what's to come.

They are called the Trench. And they are hungry.

As thousands of carnivorous beasts emerge from the ocean's depths, can Aquaman protect his people from this deadly new threat? And also the surface world that he now calls home?

This is Aquaman's renaissance—a cutting-edge revival of the King of the Seven Seas featuring the creative team behind *New York Times* best-selling graphic novels BLACKEST NIGHT and JUSTICE LEAGUE: THRONE OF ATLANTIS!

"THIS MIGHT BE [GEOFF JOHNS'] MOST IMPRESSIVE FEAT TO DATE. GENIUS." –*USA TODAY*

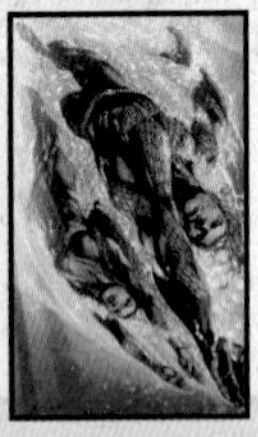

"FRESH."
–*ENTERTAINMENT WEEKLY*

"EVERY PAGE DRIPS WITH HUMOR AND ALL OF IT IS AIMED AT AQUAMAN AND HIS CONSIDERABLE CHARACTER HERITAGE, BE IT THE ORANGE SHIRT, THE POWER TO TALK TO FISH OR THE SECOND-STRING SUPERHERO STATUS." –*LOS ANGELES TIMES*

AQUAMAN VOL. 1: THE TRENCH

Writer: Geoff Johns | Artists: Ivan Reis & Joe Prado | ISBN: 978-1-4012-3710-3 | Diamond Code: FEB130206 | Price: $14.99/$17.99 CAN| Format: TP

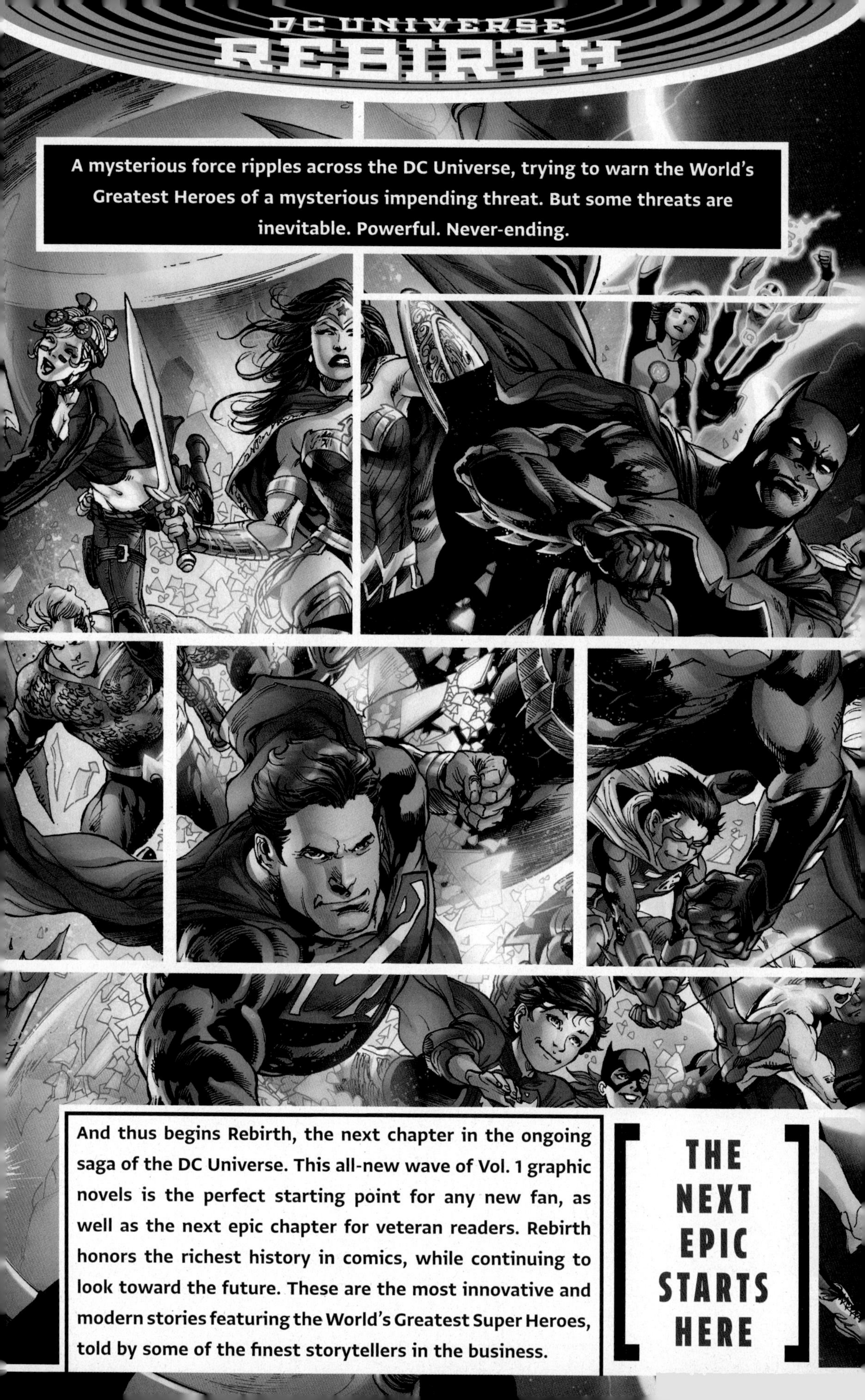
DC UNIVERSE
REBIRTH
A mysterious force ripples across the DC Universe, trying to warn the World's Greatest Heroes of a mysterious impending threat. But some threats are inevitable. Powerful. Never-ending.
And thus begins Rebirth, the next chapter in the ongoing saga of the DC Universe. This all-new wave of Vol. 1 graphic novels is the perfect starting point for any new fan, as well as the next epic chapter for veteran readers. Rebirth honors the richest history in comics, while continuing to look toward the future. These are the most innovative and modern stories featuring the World's Greatest Super Heroes, told by some of the finest storytellers in the business.
[THE NEXT EPIC STARTS HERE]

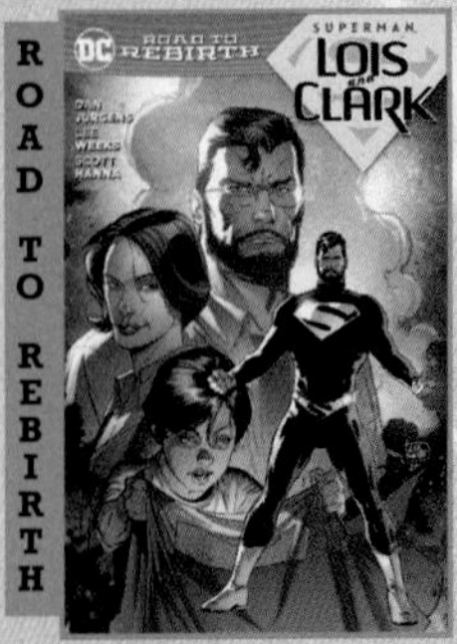

SUPERMAN: LOIS AND CLARK

From the world before FLASHPOINT, the Man of Steel and the tough-as-nails reporter find themselves and their young son, Jonathan, on a new Earth. But in a harsh world that needs saving, is it time for Superman to reveal himself?

Writer: Dan Jurgens | Artist: Lee Weeks | ISBN: 9781401262495 | Diamond Code: MAY160323
Price: $17.99/$21.99 CAN | Format: TP

TITANS HUNT

From Dan Abnett comes the series that will reveal the secret history of the Teen Titans!

Writer: Dan Abnett | Artist: Paolo Siqueirara | ISBN: 9781401265557 | Diamond Code: JUN160361
Price: $19.99/$25.99 CAN | Format: TP

SUPERMAN: THE FINAL DAYS OF SUPERMAN

It's a new chapter in the Man of Steel's life, and it will change everything you know about Superman, as the Super Hero faces his own last moments.

Writer: Peter J. Tomasi | Artists: Various | ISBN: 9781401267223 | Diamond Code: JUN160354
Price: $29.99/$39.99 CAN | Format: HC

DC UNIVERSE: REBIRTH THE DELUXE EDITION

The monumental, best-selling DC UNIVERSE: REBIRTH #1 is presented in a deluxe-edition hardcover, featuring expansive bonus material including concept sketches and variant covers!

Writer: Geoff Johns | Artists: Gary Frank, Ivan Reis, Ethan Van Sciver and Phil Jimenez | ISBN: 978-1-4012-7072-8
Diamond Code: AUG160316 | Price: $17.99/23.99 CAN | Format: HC

ACTION COMICS VOL. 1: PATH OF DOOM

A new beginning following the events of DC Rebirth sees an unlikely figure as the protector of Metropolis: Lex Luthor!

Writer: Dan Jurgens | Artists: Patrick Zircher & Tyler Kirkham | ISBN: 9781401268046 | Diamond Code: NOV160319
Price: $16.99/$19.99 CAN | Format: TP

ALL-STAR BATMAN VOL. 1: MY OWN WORST ENEMY

The #1 *New York Times* best-selling author of BATMAN, Scott Snyder, returns to the Dark Knight, this time with legendary artist John Romita Jr., as Two-Face unleashes his greatest attack ever.

Writer: Scott Snyder | Artists: John Romita Jr. & Declan Shalvey | ISBN: 9781401269784
Price: $24.99/$33.99 CAN | Format: HC | Coming April 25, 2017

AQUAMAN VOL. 1: THE DROWNING

A new era for the King of Atlantis begins as Aquaman attempts to broker peace between Atlantis and the surface world, while Black Manta launches his most lethal strike ever against his arch-foe!

Writer: Dan Abnett | Artists: Brad Walker & Phillippe Briones | ISBN: 9781401267827 | Diamond Code: OCT160290
Price: $16.99/$22.99 CAN | Format: TP

BATGIRL AND THE BIRDS OF PREY VOL. 1: WHO IS ORACLE?

Batgirl, Black Canary and Huntress reunite to hunt down Gotham's all-seeing enemy, who goes by a familiar name: Oracle!

Writers: Shawna Benson & Julie Benson | Artist: Claire Roe | ISBN: 9781401268671 | Diamond Code: MAY160212
Price: $16.99/$22.99 CAN | Format: TP | Coming April 25, 2017

BATGIRL VOL. 1: BEYOND BURNSIDE

Barbara Gordon (a.k.a. Batgirl) is leaving Burnside and hitting the road to find herself. Eisner winners Hope Larson and Raphael Albuquerque pair up to usher in a new era for beloved Babs.

Writer: Hope Larson | Artist: Rafael Albuquerque| ISBN: 9781401268404
Price: $16.99/$22.99 CAN Format: TP

BATMAN BEYOND VOL. 1: THE RETURN

The original Batman of the future, Terry McGinnis, returns to the helm as Jokerz take over part of Gotham City.

Writer: Dan Jurgens | Artists: Bernard Chang & Ryan Sook | ISBN: 9781401271039
Price: $16.99/$22.99 CAN | Format: TP | Coming July 4, 2017

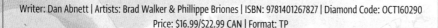

BATMAN VOL. 1: I AM GOTHAM

Batman is back in an all-new series from rising star Tom King! The Dark Knight Detective must save Gotham from its newest threat...another vigilante hero!

Writer: Tom King | Artists: David Finch & Mikel Janin | ISBN: 9781401267773
Diamond Code: OCT160291 | Price: $16.99/$22.99 CAN | Format: TP

BATMAN: NIGHT OF THE MONSTER MEN

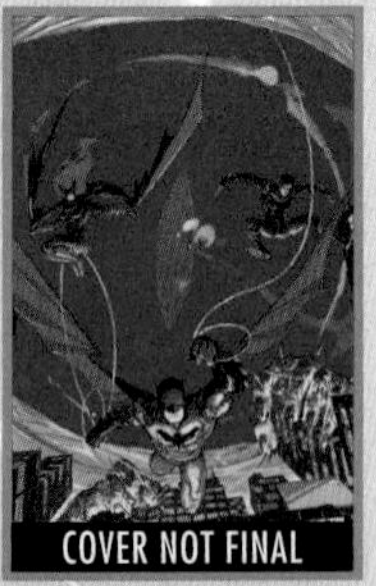

The first crossover event of the Rebirth era is here! As a huge storm approaches, Batman, Batwoman and Nightwing try to prepare Gotham for the worst, but nothing can prepare them for the monsters to come.

Writers: Tom King & Steve Orlando | Artist: Riley Rossmo | ISBN: 9781401270674 | Diamond Code: NOV160321
Price: $24.99/$33.99 | Format: HC

BLUE BEETLE VOL. 1: THE MORE THINGS CHANGE

Bonded to the Blue Beetle Scarab, Jamie Reyes tries to unlock its secrets alongside the original Blue Beetle, Ted Kord, and Doctor Fate.

Writer: Keith Giffen | Artist: Scott Kolins | ISBN: 9781401268688
Price: $16.99/$22.99 CAN | Format: TP | Coming May 16, 2017

CYBORG VOL. 1: THE IMITATION OF LIFE

Justice League member Cyborg is here in his own solo series, and he's beginning his greatest quest to date: to find his soul...if he has one!

Writer: John Semper Jr. | Artists: Will Conrad & Paul Pelletier | ISBN: 9781401267926
Price: $16.99/$22.99 CAN | Format: TP

DEATHSTROKE VOL. 1: THE PROFESSIONAL

Slade Wilson, a.k.a. Deathstroke, just got a new contract. The trouble is, the people on his hit list are his closest family and confidants!

Writer: Christopher Priest | Artist: Carlo Pagulayan | ISBN: 9781401268237
Price: $16.99/$22.99 CAN | Format: TP

BATMAN - DETECTIVE COMICS VOL. 1: THE RISE OF THE BATMEN

Gotham needs more than just the Bat. First cousins Batman and Batwoman pair up to train new and familiar vigilante recruits in the fight against an army of mysterious foes!

Writer: James Tynion IV | Artists: Eddy Barrows & Alvaro Martinez | ISBN: 9781401267995 | Diamond Code: NOV160317
Price: $16.99/$22.99 CAN | Format: TP

THE FLASH VOL. 1: LIGHTNING STRIKES TWICE

Rising star writer Joshua Williamson heralds in a new era for the Flash, who finds himself in a city of speedsters after a familiar lightning storm.

Writer: Joshua Williamson | Artists: Carmine Di Giandomenico & Neil Googe | ISBN: 9781401267841 |
Diamond Code: OCT160292 | Price: $17.99/$23.99 CAN | Format: TP

GREEN ARROW VOL. 1: THE DEATH & LIFE OF OLIVER QUEEN

Oliver Queen is back in Seattle to uncover an illegal human trafficking operation when he comes face-to-face with a familiar yet mysterious love—Black Canary!

Writer: Benjamin Percy | Artists: Otto Schmidt & Juan Ferreyra | ISBN: 9781401267810
Diamond Code: OCT160293 | Price: $16.99/$22.99 CAN | Format: TP

GREEN LANTERNS VOL. 1: RAGE PLANET

Rookie Green Lanterns Jessica Cruz and Simon Baz must overcome their clashing personalities and tackle the universe's toughest beat: Earth!

Writer: Sam Humphries | Artist: Robson Rocha | ISBN: 9781401267759 | Diamond Code: OCT160294
Price: $16.99/$22.99 CAN | Format: TP

HAL JORDAN & THE GREEN LANTERN CORPS VOL. 1: SINESTRO'S LAW

Robert Venditti launches a new era of Hal Jordan and the Corps as they must rise up against the new force of justice in the universe: the Sinestro Corps!

Writer: Robert Venditti | Artists: Ethan Van Sciver & Rafa Sandoval | ISBN: 9781401268008
Diamond Code: NOV160318 | Price: $16.99/$22.99 CAN | Format: TP

HARLEY QUINN VOL. 1: DIE LAUGHING

Jimmy Palmiotti and Amanda Conner spearhead Harley's return in the wake of DC Rebirth as her crazy world gets even crazier.

Writers: Jimmy Palmiotti & Amanda Conner | Artists: Chad Hardin & John Timms | ISBN: 9781401268312
Price: $16.99/$22.99 CAN | Format: TP

THE HELLBLAZER VOL. 1: THE POISON TRUTH

Back in his hometown of London, John Constantine—now teaming with Swamp Thing—finds himself with a choice: save his soul and risk the lives of millions of people, or continue on as the Hellblazer!

Writer: Simon Oliver | Artist: Moritat | ISBN: 9781401268862
Price: $16.99/$22.99 CAN | Format: TP | Coming April 4, 2017

JUSTICE LEAGUE VOL. 1: THE EXTINCTION MACHINES

Following DC Rebirth, the World's Greatest Super Heroes—the Justice League—come together again to face new, more devastating threats!

Writer: Bryan Hitch | Artist: Tony S. Daniel | ISBN: 9781401267797 | Diamond Code: OCT160295
Price: $16.99/$22.99 CAN | Format: TP

NEW SUPER-MAN VOL. 1: MADE IN CHINA

The #1 *New York Times* best-selling author Gene Luen Yang introduces a new Man of Steel, created by the Chinese government. But the government may have chosen the wrong person for the job.

Writer: Gene Luen Yang | Artist: Viktor Bogdanovic | ISBN: 9781401270933
Price: $16.99/$22.99 CAN | Format: TP | Coming June 27, 2017

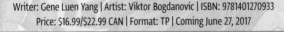

NIGHTWING VOL. 1: BETTER THAN BATMAN

Nightwing is back! Boy Wonder turned vigilante turned super-spy Dick Grayson returns to take down the international Parliament of Owls!

Writer: Tim Seeley | Artist: Javier Fernández | ISBN: 9781401268039 | Diamond Code: OCT160296
Price: $16.99/$22.99 CAN | Format: TP

RED HOOD & THE OUTLAWS VOL. 1: DARK TRINITY

Red Hood embraces his bad side and looks to take down the crime lord Black Mask with the help of his new Outsiders: Bizarro and Artemis.

Writer: Scott Lobdell | Artist: Dexter Soy | ISBN: 9781401268756
Price: $16.99/$22.99 CAN | Format: TP | Coming May 2, 2017

SUICIDE SQUAD VOL. 1: THE BLACK VAULT

From Rob Williams, superstar artist Jim Lee and Philip Tan comes the new Suicide Squad—Harley Quinn, Deadshot, Captain Boomerang, Katana and Killer Croc!

Writer: Rob Williams | Artists: Jim Lee & Philip Tan | ISBN: 9781401269814
Price: $16.99/$22.99 CAN | Format: TP

SUPERGIRL VOL. 1: REIGN OF THE CYBORG SUPERMEN

Supergirl moves to National City in this new series, perfect for fans of the hit TV show, now on The CW.

Writer: Steve Orlando | Artist: Brian Ching | ISBN: 9781401268466
Price: $16.99/$22.99 CAN | Format: TP | Coming May 2, 2017

SUPERMAN VOL. 1: SON OF SUPERMAN

A new Superman appears to protect the world while raising a super-son with his wife, Lois Lane.

Writers: Peter J. Tomasi & Patrick Gleason | Artists: Patrick Gleason & Doug Mahnke
ISBN: 9781401267766 | Diamond Code: OCT160297 | Price: $16.99/$22.99 CAN | Format: TP

SUPERWOMAN VOL. 1: WHO KILLED SUPERWOMAN?

The newly super-powered Lois Lane must take on the task of being the protector of Metropolis. The only problem is, her newfound powers are killing her!

Writer: Phil Jimenez | Artist: Phil Jimenez | ISBN: 9781401267803
Price: $16.99/$22.99 CAN | Format: TP | Coming May 9, 2017

TEEN TITANS VOL. 1: DAMIAN KNOWS BEST

Robin, a.k.a. Damian Wayne, puts together a new team of Teen Titans to take down his own grandfather, Ra's al Ghul!

Writer: Benjamin Percy | Artist: Jonboy Meyers | ISBN: 9781401270773
Price: $16.99/$22.99 CAN | Format: TP | Coming June 13, 2017

TITANS VOL. 1: THE RETURN OF WALLY WEST

Fan-favorite speedster Wally West is back in the DCU! But what does this mean for the rest of the classic Titans lineup?

Writer: Dan Abnett | Artist: Brett Booth | ISBN: 9781401268176
Price: $16.99/$22.99 CAN | Format: TP

TRINITY VOL. 1: BETTER TOGETHER

New York Times best-selling creator Francis Manapul unites Batman, Superman and Wonder Woman to protect the planet from threats too big for just one Super Hero.

Writer: Francis Manapul | Artists: Francis Manapul & Clay Mann | ISBN: 9781401270766
Diamond Code: TK | Price: $24.99/$33.99 CAN | Format: HC | Coming June 13, 2017

WONDER WOMAN VOL. 1: THE LIES

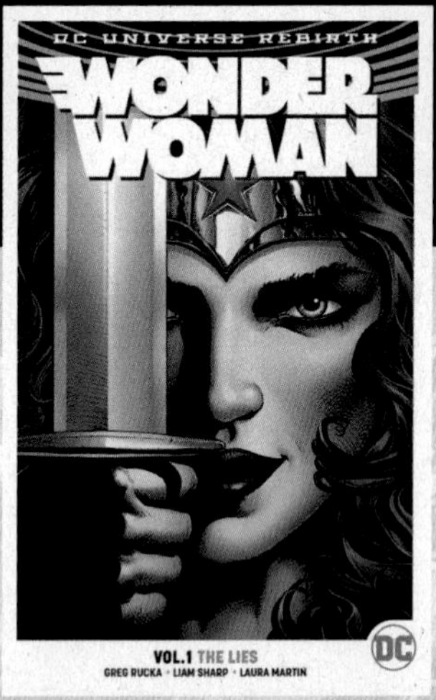

New York Times best-selling writer Greg Rucka returns to Wonder Woman with a tale that will forever alter the DC icon.

Writer: Greg Rucka | Artist: Liam Sharp | ISBN: 9781401267780 | Diamond Code: NOV160320
Price: $16.99/$22.99 CAN | Format: TP

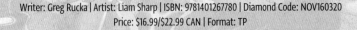

JUSTICE LEAGUE vs. SUICIDE SQUAD

Two of the DC Universe's most powerful superteams square off in this event graphic novel written by rising star Joshua Williamson.

Writer: Joshua Williamson | Artists: Various | ISBN: 9781401272265
Price: $39.99/$53.99 CAN | Format: HC | Coming June 27, 2017

MODERN CLASSICS

WATCHMEN, BATMAN: THE KILLING JOKE, DC: THE NEW FRONTIER. These graphic novels are now embedded in the very fabric of the comics industry, heralded as the best the genre has to offer. But all classics must have their beginnings. The following graphic novels are the next in line at DC, as top creators of recent years deliver innovative, poignant stories, with subject matter ranging from superheroes to love stories to autobiographical true crime. Pushing the boundaries of their respective genres and using the comics medium to maximum effect, each of these titles is a contemporary masterpiece in its own way.

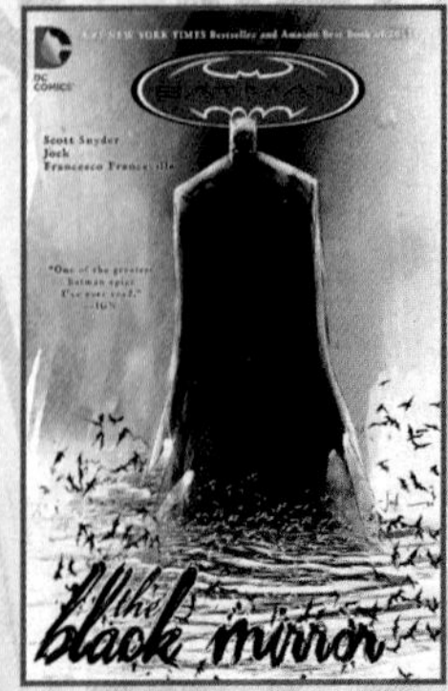

BATMAN: THE BLACK MIRROR

Eisner Award-winning writer Scott Snyder launches into comics superstardom with his #1 *New York Times* best-selling debut work on the Dark Knight.

A series of brutal murders pushes Batman's detective skills to the limit and forces him to confront one of Gotham City's oldest evils. Helpless and trapped in the deadly Mirror House, Batman must fight for his life against a villain from his past that he never sees coming.

"ONE OF THE BEST NEW COLLABORATIONS IN COMICS...THIS IS A WORTHY SPIRITUAL SUCCESSOR TO BATMAN: YEAR ONE." –MTV GEEK

Writer: Scott Snyder | Artists: Jock & Francesco Francavilla | ISBN: 978-1-4012-3207-8 | Diamond Code: NOV120268| Price: $16.99/$19.99 CAN | Format: TP

BATMAN: ARKHAM ASYLUM

"[A] DARKLY POETIC, PSYCHOLOGICALLY RICH TALE." –ROLLING STONE

The psychologically twisted celebration of Batman's rogues gallery that launched Grant Morrison's career and inspired one of the hottest video games of all time.

After striking a deal with the Joker to free a group of hostages, Batman is lobbed out of his comfort zone on the streets of Gotham and locked away with Arkham's most psychotic inmates. Surrounded by a fortress of grit and an onslaught of his most deranged enemies, the Dark Knight faces an unprecedented fight to stay in control of both body and mind.

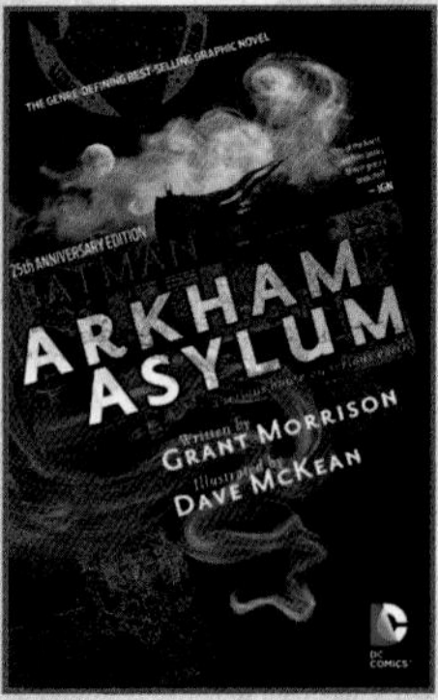

Writer: Grant Morrison | Artist: Dave McKean | ISBN: 978-1-4012-5124-6 | Diamond Code: JUN140278 | Price: $19.99 / $23.99 CAN | Format: TP

BLACKEST NIGHT

Geoff Johns and Ivan Reis craft an unforgettable ensemble of undead superheroes in this highly anticipated and shockingly stylized blockbuster brawl.

The Black Lanterns are the scourge of the universe—and they won't stop at gravedigging to secure dominance. Led by Nekron and Black Hand, the Lanterns look to boost their sinister ranks by resurrecting and assembling an army of fallen superheroes—from Aquaman and Superman to Green Arrow—to support a vicious crusade against humankind.

"IF YOU'VE READ A SUPERHERO COMIC BOOK PUBLISHED BY DC COMICS WITHIN THE LAST FEW YEARS, AND WERE COMPLETELY BLOWN AWAY BY IT, THERE'S A GOOD CHANCE THAT IT WAS SOMETHING WRITTEN BY GEOFF JOHNS." –WASHINGTON EXAMINER

Writer: Geoff Johns | Artist: Ivan Reis | ISBN: 978-1-4012-2953-5 | Diamond Code: APR110192 | Price: $19.99/$23.99 CAN | Format: TP

DARK NIGHT: A TRUE BATMAN STORY

"THIS GRAPHIC NOVEL STANDS AS ONE OF THE BRAVEST, MOST VULNERABLE WORKS OF THE MEDIUM IN YEARS..." –PASTE MAGAZINE

In this autobiographical true story, *Batman: The Animated Series* creator Paul Dini recounts a harrowing beating and road to recovery through the eyes of the Dark Knight.

In the 1990s, legendary writer Paul Dini was walking home one evening and was viciously beaten within an inch of his life. His recovery process was arduous, hampered by the imagined antics of the villains he was writing for television, including the Joker, Harley Quinn and the Penguin. Despite how bleak his circumstances were, or perhaps because of it, Dini also always imagined the Batman at his side, chivvying him along during his darkest moments.

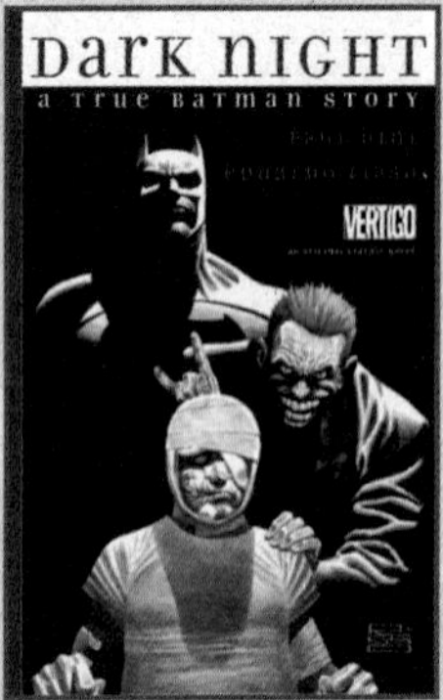

Writer: Paul Dini | Artist: Eduardo Risso | ISBN: 9781401241438 | Diamond Code: FEB160250 | Price: $22.99/$27.99 CAN | Format: HC | FOR MATURE READERS

DAYTRIPPER

This Eisner Award-winning graphic novel follows Bras de Oliva Dominguez during different periods in his life, each with the same ending: his death.

In DAYTRIPPER, the Eisner Award-winning twin brothers Fabio Moon and Gabriel Ba tell a magical, mysterious and moving story about life itself—a hauntingly lyrical journey that uses the quiet moments to ask the big questions.

Truly one of the most original and compelling graphic novels of the last decade, DAYTRIPPER is an affecting, memorable story that will stay with readers long after they've finished reading.

"MIXED WITH THE EXPERT CRAFTSMANSHIP OF TWO ARTISTS IN THEIR PRIME TELLING A UNIQUE STORY IN A REMARKABLE WAY, THE INDUSTRY MAY HAVE JUST CRAFTED ITS LATEST WATCHMEN." -POP MATTERS

Writers: Gabriel Bá & Fabío Moon | Artists: Gabriel Bá & Fabío Moon | ISBN: 978-14012-2969-6 | Diamond Code: NOV100268
Price: $19.99/$23.99 CAN | Format: TP | FOR MATURE READERS

"FROM THE FERTILE MIND OF WRITER GRANT MORRISON... THIS [IS] THE EVENT TO TRUMP ALL EVENTS." -ENTERTAINMENT WEEKLY

FINAL CRISIS

Grant Morrison transforms the DC Universe in this monumental crossover event years in the making.

Evil has finally won. Darkseid and his legion have claimed a devastating victory in a time-bending war between light and dark, forcing Batman, Superman and the Justice League to face the fallout and adjust to a new apocalyptic reality. Experimental, vivid and relentless, this epic explores what happens when the world's most imposing superheroes are stripped of their powers—and their hope.

Writer: Grant Morrison | Artists: J.G. Jones, Doug Mahnke & Carlos Pacheco | ISBN: 9781401245177 | Diamond Code: JAN140352
Price: $19.99/$23.99 CAN | Format: TP

FOREVER EVIL

Acclaimed creators Geoff Johns and David Finch spearhead this *New York Times* best-selling, universe-wide crossover event in a groundbreaking transformation of villains into antiheroes.

The Crime Syndicate—a twisted, villainous version of the Justice League—has taken over the world in search of new recruits. With the Justice League eliminated, it's up to Lex Luthor, Batman and his legion of super-villains to protect the planet from falling to an even greater evil in this giant crossover event!

"GEOFF JOHNS' BEST WORK SINCE THE NEW 52 BEGAN... A BLAST TO READ." -NERDIST

Writer: Geoff Johns | Artist: David Finch | ISBN: 978-1-4012-5338-7 | Diamond Code: FEB150254 | Price: $19.99/$23.99 CAN | Format: TP

"GET JIRO! IS ONE OF THE YEAR'S MOST UNUSUAL COMIC-BOOK PROJECTS, AND ALSO ONE OF THE MOST FUN." -A.V. CLUB/THE ONION

GET JIRO!

Anthony Bourdain, top chef and star of the hit travel show *No Reservations*, and Joel Rose co-write this *New York Times* best-selling graphic novel send-up of food culture and society.

In a not-too-distant future L.A. where master chefs rule the town like crime lords and people literally kill for a seat at the best restaurants, a bloody culinary war is raging. When a renegade and ruthless sushi chef named Jiro is sought after by the warring factions, no chef may be left alive!

Writers: Anthony Bourdain & Joel Rose | Artist: Langdon Foss | ISBN: 978-1-4012-2828-6 | Diamond Code: FEB130242
Price: $14.99/$17.99 CAN | Format: TP | FOR MATURE READERS

GREEN ARROW VOL. 4: THE KILL MACHINE

The Emerald Archer is brought back to his roots by the indomitable creative team of Jeff Lemire and Andrea Sorrentino.

Oliver Queen thought he had it all figured out. As the heroic archer Green Arrow, he'd finally found a sense of purpose, friends to aid him, even a place in the Justice League of America. But when a mysterious enemy from his past comes to the surface, everything Oliver thought he knew about himself and his family is thrown into the fire.

"JEFF LEMIRE AND ANDREA SORRENTINO HIT THE BULLS-EYE PERFECTLY WITH GREEN ARROW." -CRAVEONLINE

Writer: Jeff Lemire | Artist: Andrea Sorrentino | ISBN: 978-1-4012-4690-7 | Diamond Code: DEC130306
Price: $16.99/$19.99 CAN | Format: TP

IDENTITY CRISIS

***New York Times* best-selling novelist Brad Meltzer teams with critically acclaimed artist Rags Morales to deliver one of the most intimate and heartbreaking graphic novels of all time.**

After a grisly murder rocks the DC Universe, the entire superhero community searches for the killer. But before the mystery is solved, a number of long-buried secrets will threaten to divide the Justice League.

"THE *IDENTITY CRISIS* MYSTERY INVOLVES THE BIGGEST DC HEROES AND WILL USE ALL OF MR. MELTZER'S SKILLS AS A THRILLER NOVELIST."
–*NEW YORK TIMES*

Writer: Brad Meltzer | Artist: Rags Morales | ISBN: 978-1-4012-6313-3 | Diamond Code: NOV150278 | Price: $19.99/$23.99 CAN | Format: TP

"DISTURBING, VIOLENT, ODDLY PSYCHOLOGICAL AND INSANELY WONDERFUL."
–*USA TODAY*

JOKER

Eisner Award winner Brian Azzarello and Lee Bermejo's original graphic novel masterpiece with a never-before-told perspective on the most vile, dangerous and unpredictable inmate of Arkham—the Joker!

The Joker has been mysteriously released from Arkham Asylum, and he's not too happy about what's happened to his town while he's been away. What follows is a harrowing night of revenge, murder and manic crime, as he brutally takes back his stolen assets from the Penguin, Riddler, Two-Face, Killer Croc and, of course, the Batman.

Writer: Brian Azzarello | Artist: Lee Bermejo | ISBN: 9781401215811 | Diamond Code: JUL080124 | Price: $19.99/$23.99 CAN | Format: HC

KINGDOM COME

Old and new eras of superheroes are pitted against each other in this epic graphic novel.

Set in the not-so-distant future, the DC Universe is spinning inexorably out of control. The new generation of heroes has lost its moral compass, becoming just as reckless and violent as the villains its members fight. The previous regime of heroes—the Justice League—returns under the most dire of circumstances, setting up a battle of the old guard against these uncompromising protectors in a battle that will define what heroism truly is.

"WAID'S CHARGED DIALOGUE AND ROSS' STUNNING VISUAL REALISM EXPOSE THE GENIUS, PRIDE, FEARS AND FOIBLES OF DC'S HEROES AND VILLAINS."
–*WASHINGTON POST*

Writer: Mark Waid | Artist: Alex Ross | ISBN: 9781401220341 | Diamond Code: SEP138294 | Price: $19.99/$23.99 CAN | Format: TP

"DOING 'BIG' AND 'GRAND' IS MORRISON'S GREATEST STRENGTH AS A WRITER, AND *THE MULTIVERSITY* IS THE OPUS HE'S BEEN WORKING ON NOW FOR OVER FIVE YEARS."
–NERDIST

THE MULTIVERSITY

Visionary Grant Morrison's expansive introduction to the alternate Earths of the DC Multiverse!

Travel beyond the familiar DC Universe and come face to face with the Vampire League of Earth-43, the Justice Riders of Earth-18, Superdemon, Doc Fate, the super-sons of Superman and Batman, the rampaging Retaliators of Earth-8, the Atomic Knights of Justice, Dino-Cop and more. In this cosmos-spanning, soul-shaking saga, you're on the frontline in the battle for all creation against the demonic destroyers known as the Gentry.

Writer: Grant Morrison | Artists: Frank Quitely, Ivan Reis, Jim Lee, et al. | ISBN: 9781401265250 | Diamond Code: AUG160336
Price: $29.99/$39.99 CAN | Format: TP

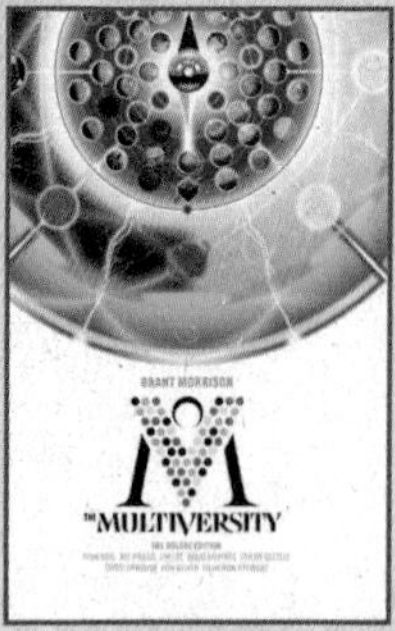

OMEGA MEN: THE END IS HERE

On the precipice of stardom, writer Tom King brings together a space opera teeming with complex themes, genuine emotion and contemporary subject matter.

The Omega Men, an alleged terrorist cell, have killed Kyle Rayner, the White Lantern. But are they really the universe's biggest threat? Or are they the only hope for freedom this godforsaken sector of the universe has? The truth is much more complicated than it seems in this story—a true definition of a modern classic.

"KING HAS TAKEN AN OBSCURE SUPER-TEAM AND REINVENTED THEM IN A BOLD, EXCITING WAY."
-IGN

Writer: Tom King | Artist: Barnaby Bagenda | ISBN: 978-1-4012-6153-5 | Diamond Code: MAY160316 | Price: $24.99/ $29.99 CAN | Format: TP

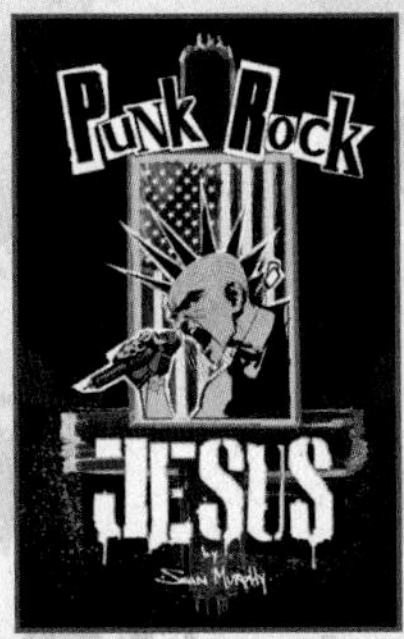

PUNK ROCK JESUS

Written and illustrated by award-winning creator Sean Murphy, PUNK ROCK JESUS brilliantly deconstructs modern society, embraces the punk aesthetic, and takes readers on an epic, emotional ride, three chords at a time.

J2 has created the ultimate reality show stunt: create a human clone from DNA lifted off the Shroud of Turin, implant it in the womb of a virginal teen mom—and give birth, on live TV, to a boy who could be the second coming of Jesus Christ Himself.

"PUNK ROCK JESUS IS AMAZING. THE SERIES HAS BEEN INCREDIBLE RIGHT FROM THE BEGINNING AND IT ENDS IN A SPECTACULAR FASHION. IT'S BRILLIANT AND HEARTBREAKING, EPIC AND EMOTIONAL...THIS IS A BOOK THAT MAKES YOU THINK." -IGN

Writer: Sean Murphy | Artist: Sean Murphy | ISBN: 978-1-4012-3768-4 | Diamond Code: JAN130330 | Price: $16.99/$19.99 CAN
Format: TP | FOR MATURE READERS

"IT'S A VISUALLY STRIKING BOOK WITH AN EQUALLY ENGAGING STORY, CHANNELING THE SPIRIT OF CLASSIC VERTIGO WHILE STILL DELIVERING SOMETHING FRESH AND EXCITING." -A.V. CLUB/THE ONION

SHERIFF OF BABYLON VOL. 1: BANG. BANG. BANG.

Inspired by his real-life experiences as a CIA operations officer in Iraq, Tom King delivers a wartime crime thriller like no other.

Baghdad, 2003. The reign of Saddam Hussein is over. The Americans are in command. And no one is in control. Former cop turned military contractor Christopher Henry knows that better than anyone. He's in the country to train a new Iraqi police force, and one of his recruits has just been murdered. With civil authority in tatters and dead bodies clogging the streets, Chris is the only person in the Green Zone with any interest in finding out who killed him—and why.

Writer: Tom King | Artist: Mitch Gerads | ISBN: 978-1-4012-6466-6 | Diamond Code: APR160424 | Price: $14.99/ $17.99 CAN | Format: TP
FOR MATURE READERS

SUPERMAN: AMERICAN ALIEN

A #1 *New York Times* bestseller! Hollywood screenwriter and Eisner Award nominee Max Landis joins forces with top comics illustrators to create a new epic that chronicles the life of Clark Kent.

These are not the stories of the iconic "Superman" as you know him. Clark Kent is a soft-spoken, charming, often-funny Kansas farm boy behind the Man of Steel. With the tone of each issue ranging from heartwarming and simple, to frighteningly gritty and violent, to sexy, sun-kissed and funny, SUPERMAN: AMERICAN ALIEN is unlike anything you've seen before.

"CINEMATIC AND EMOTIONAL... THE RIGHT BALANCE OF FRESH AND TOUCHING." -NEW YORK DAILY NEWS

Writer: Max Landis | Artists: Francis Manapul, Jae Lee, Nick Dragotta, Jock, et al. | ISBN: 978-1-4012-6256-3
Diamond Code: JUN160357 | Price: $24.99/ $29.99 | Format: HC

"RED SON IS ONE OF THOSE RARE PROJECTS THAT BRIDGES THE GAP BETWEEN GENERATIONS AND ILLUSTRATES WHY COMICS–AND THE MOVIES BASED ON THEM–ARE STILL FRESH AND FULL OF SURPRISES FOR NEW AND OLD FANS ALIKE." -IFC

SUPERMAN: RED SON

What if the rocket from Krypton carrying the infant Superman landed in the midst of 1950s Soviet Union?

In this startling twist on a familiar tale, a certain Kryptonian rocket ship crash-lands on Earth carrying an infant who will one day become the most powerful being on the planet. But his ship doesn't land in America. Instead, he makes his new home on a collective in the Soviet Union. As the young alien becomes a symbol to the Soviet people, the world changes drastically from what we know—bringing Superman into conflict with Batman, Lex Luthor and more.

Writer: Mark Millar | Artists: Dave Johnson & Kilian Plunkett | ISBN: 978-1-4012-4711-9 | Diamond Code: JAN140353
Price: $17.99/$20.99 CAN | Format: TP

TRILLIUM

Eisner Award-nominated writer/artist Jeff Lemire reinvents the concept of a love story in the medium in this visually innovative and mind-expanding tale.

Two disparate souls are separated by thousands of years and hundreds of millions of miles. Yet they will fall in love and, as a result, bring about the end of the universe. Even though reality is unraveling all around them, nothing can pull them apart. This isn't just a love story: it's the last love story ever told.

"I'M BEWILDERED AND INTRIGUED BY THE TALE THAT'S UNFOLDING, IN AWE OF LEMIRE'S WRITING AND ART AND EXCITED BY THE STRUCTURAL PLAYFULNESS AT WORK." -MTV GEEK

Writer: Jeff Lemire | Artist: Jeff Lemire | ISBN: 978-1-4012-4900-7 | Diamond Code: MAY140407 | Price: $16.99/$19.99 CAN
Format: TP | FOR MATURE READERS

BATMAN

Dark Knight. Caped Crusader. World's Greatest Detective. Whatever you know him as, Batman is proof you don't need superpowers to be a superhero. As a child, Bruce Wayne helplessly watched as his parents were brutally murdered in front of him. From that day forth, Bruce vowed to wage a one-man war on crime, donning the cape and the cowl to become Batman. Created by Bob Kane with Bill Finger in 1939, Batman made his debut in the pages of DETECTIVE COMICS #27 and has since become a fixture in popular culture the world over.

- BATMAN: YEAR ONE
- BATMAN: THE LONG HALLOWEEN
- BATMAN: DARK VICTORY
- BATMAN: THE KILLING JOKE
- BATMAN: KNIGHTFALL
- BATMAN: HUSH
- BATMAN: BATMAN & SON
- FINAL CRISIS
- BATMAN & ROBIN: BATMAN REBORN
- BATMAN: THE BLACK MIRROR

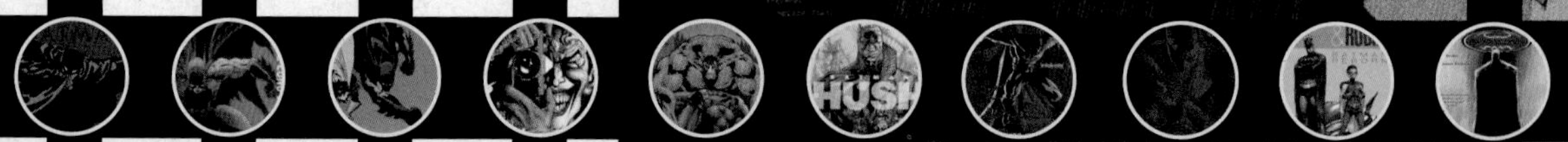

FLASHPOINT
BATMAN: ZERO YEAR
BATMAN: THE COURT OF OWLS
BATMAN: NIGHT OF THE OWLS
BATMAN: A DEATH IN THE FAMILY
BATMAN ETERNAL
BATMAN: ENDGAME
BATMAN: SUPERHEAVY
BATMAN: REBIRTH

BATMAN: THE GOLDEN AGE VOL. 1

The original adventures of the Dark Knight that made the character a pop icon the world over.

Writer: Bill Finger | Artist: Bob Kane
ISBN: 9781401263331 | Diamond Code: MAY160305
Price: $24.99/$29.99 | Format: TP

BATMAN: YEAR ONE

Frank Miller's genre-defining graphic novel detailing a rookie Dark Knight's first year in Gotham City.

Writer: Frank Miller | Artist: David Mazzucchelli
ISBN: 978-1-4012-0752-6 | Diamond Code: OCT060163
Price: $14.99/$17.99 CAN | Format: TP

BATMAN: THE LONG HALLOWEEN

A Batman murder mystery written by Jeph Loeb with art by Tim Sale, set during the Dark Knight's early days as he must race against the calendar to discover the identity of the serial killer, Holiday.

Writer: Jeph Loeb | Artist: Tim Sale
ISBN: 978-1-4012-3259-7 | Diamond Code: JUL110251
Price: $24.99/$28.99 CAN | Format: TP

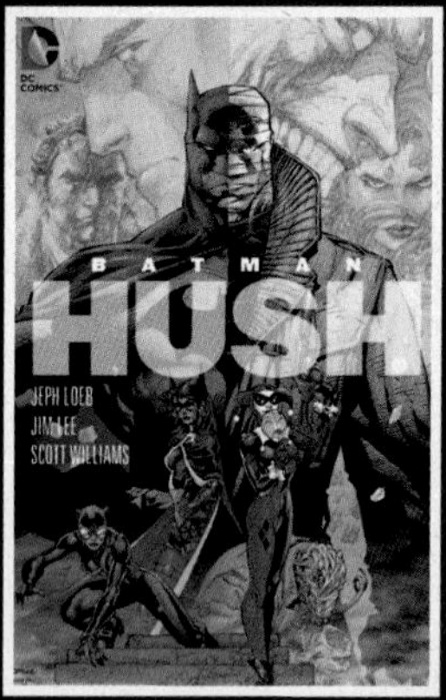

BATMAN: DARK VICTORY

In this sequel to BATMAN: THE LONG HALLOWEEN, Batman faces another seemingly unsolvable mystery, as the Hangman runs through a murder spree in Gotham City.

Writer: Jeph Loeb | Artist: Tim Sale
ISBN: 978-1-4012-4401-9 | Diamond Code: NOV130237
Price: $24.99/$28.99 CAN | Format: TP

BATMAN: ARKHAM ASYLUM 25th ANNIVERSARY EDITION

Grant Morrison and Dave McKean's psychological horror story from Arkham Asylum, home to Gotham City's most deranged super-criminals

Writer: Grant Morrison | Artist: Dave McKean
ISBN: 978-1-4012-5124-6 | Diamond Code: JUN140278
Price: $19.99/$23.99 CAN | Format: TP

BATMAN: THE KILLING JOKE

The Joker, Batman's greatest adversary, in his definitive origin story by Alan Moore with breathtaking art by Brian Bolland.

Writer: Alan Moore | Artist: Brian Bolland
ISBN: 978-1-4012-1667-2 | Diamond Code: NOV070226
Price: $17.99/$20.99 CAN | Format: HC
FOR MATURE READERS

BATMAN: KNIGHTFALL VOL. 1

Batman's entire rogues gallery is freed from Arkham Asylum by the villainous Bane, who tests the Dark Knight mentally and physically as never before.

Writers: Various | Artists: Various
ISBN: 978-1-4012-3379-2 | Diamond Code: JAN120303
Price: $29.99/$35.00 CAN | Format: TP

BATMAN: HUSH

The all-star team of Jeph Loeb and Jim Lee traces the tale of Batman as he seeks to stop a new and deadly villain who seems to know more about Batman than anyone—Hush!

Writer: Jeph Loeb | Artist: Jim Lee
ISBN: 978-1-4012-2317-5 | Diamond Code: MAY090178
Price: $24.99/$28.99 CAN | Format: TP

BATMAN & SON

In Grant Morrison's epic Batman run, Bruce discovers that he's sired a son, Damian Wayne. Also included is BATMAN: THE BLACK GLOVE by Morrison with art by J.H. Williams III.

Writer: Grant Morrison Artists: Andy Kubert, J.H. Williams III & Tony S. Daniel
ISBN: 978-1-4012-4402-6 | Diamond Code: OCT130238
Price: $19.99/$23.99 CAN Format: TP

BATMAN & ROBIN VOL. 1: BATMAN REBORN

The dynamic duo is reborn, with Dick Grayson donning the cape and cowl along with new Robin Damian Wayne.

Writer: Grant Morrison | Artist: Frank Quitely
ISBN: 978-1-4012-2987-0 | Diamond Code: DEC100246
Price: $14.99/$17.99 CAN | Format: TP

BATMAN INCORPORATED

Batman deputizes different "Batmen" in nations around the globe, creating the unstoppable Batman Incorporated.

Writer: Grant Morrison | Artist: Yanick Paquette
ISBN: 978-1-4012-3827-8 | Diamond Code: OCT120258
Price: $19.99/$23.99 CAN | Format: TP

BATMAN: THE BLACK MIRROR

The past comes back to haunt Commissioner Gordon and Batman by way of a diabolic murder mystery, in this dark graphic novel that launched writer Scott Snyder into superstardom.

Writer: Scott Snyder | Artists: Jock & Francesco Francavilla
ISBN: 978-1-4012-3206-1 | Diamond Code: NOV120268
Price: $16.99/$34.99 CAN | Format: TP

BATMAN VOL. 1: THE COURT OF OWLS

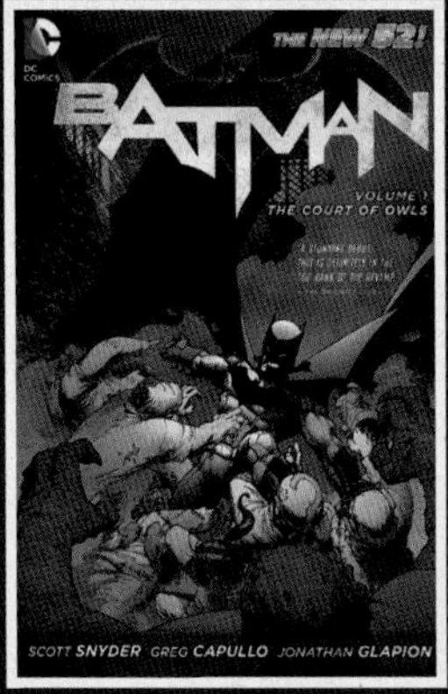

A new era for the Dark Knight and Gotham City begins here from writer Scott Snyder and artist Greg Capullo, as Batman and the Bat-family continue their quest to protect the people of Gotham.

Writer: Scott Snyder | Artist: Greg Capullo
ISBN: 978-1-4012-3542-0 | Diamond Code: DEC120323
Price: $16.99/$19.99 CAN | Format: TP

BATMAN VOL. 2: CITY OF OWLS

NIGHT OF THE OWLS continues here! Batman must stop the TALONS that have breached the Batcave in order to save an innocent life...and Gotham City!

Writer: Scott Snyder | Artists: Greg Capullo & Rafael Albuquerque | ISBN: 978-1-4012-3778-3 | Diamond Code: JUL130235 | Price: $16.99/$19.99 CAN | Format: TP

BATMAN VOL. 3: DEATH OF THE FAMILY

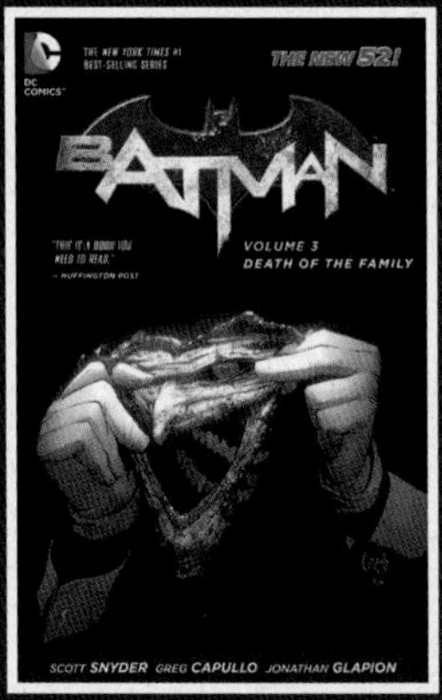

After having his face sliced off one year ago, the Joker makes his horrifying return to Gotham City! How can Batman protect his city and those he's closest to?

Writer: Scott Snyder | Artists: Greg Capullo & Jock
ISBN: 978-1-4012-4602-0 | Diamond Code: FEB140248
Price: $16.99/$19.99 CAN | Format: TP

BATMAN VOL. 4: ZERO YEAR-SECRET CITY

Scott Snyder and Greg Capullo present an astonishing new vision of the Dark Knight's origin—and his first encounters with the Riddler, the Red Hood and others!

Writer: Scott Snyder | Artist: Greg Capullo
ISBN: 978-1-4012-4933-5 | Diamond Code: JUL140237
Price: $16.99/$19.99 CAN | Format: TP

BATMAN VOL. 5: ZERO YEAR-DARK CITY

Scott Snyder and Greg Capullo conclude their amazing new take on the Dark Knight's beginnings!

Writer: Scott Snyder | Artist: Greg Capullo
ISBN: 978-1-4012-5335-6 | Diamond Code: JAN150363
Price: $16.99/$19.99 CAN | Format: TP

BATMAN VOL. 6: GRAVEYARD SHIFT

In the wake of the death of his son, Damian, Batman is in danger of losing his humanity.

Writer: Scott Snyder | Artist: Greg Capullo
ISBN: 978-1-4012-5753-8 | Diamond Code: JUN150290
Price: $16.99/$19.99 CAN | Format: TP

BATMAN VOL. 7: ENDGAME

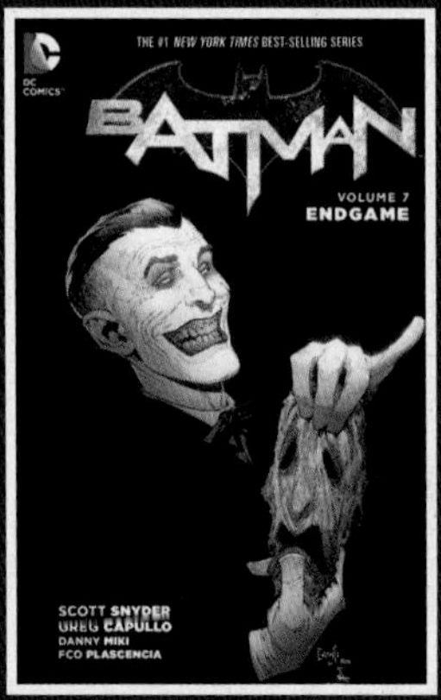

The Joker is out to finally destroy Batman for good as Scott Snyder and Greg Capullo tell their definitive Joker story with an ending you have to see to believe!

Writer: Scott Snyder | Artist: Greg Capullo
ISBN: 978-1-4012-6116-0 | Diamond Code: DEC150331
Price: $19.99/$23.99 CAN | Format: TP

BATMAN VOL. 8: SUPERHEAVY

In the most daring chapter of their best-selling run, Snyder and Capullo bring an all-new Batman on the scene in Gotham City.

Writer: Scott Snyder | Artist: Greg Capullo
ISBN: 9781401266301 | Diamond Code: JUN160332
Price: $16.99/$22.99 CAN | Format: TP

BATMAN VOL. 9: BLOOM

In the conclusion to their epic saga, the mammoth creative team of Snyder and Capullo bring Bruce Wayne back to the cape and cowl.

Writer: Scott Snyder | Artist: Greg Capullo
ISBN: 9781401266301 | Diamond Code: SEP160335
Price: $16.99/$22.99 CAN | Format: TP

BATMAN VOL. 10: EPILOGUE

Batman must pick up the pieces of a broken Gotham City in the wake of Mr. Bloom's attack.

Writer: Scott Snyder & James Tynion IV
Artist: Greg Capullo, Riley Rossmo, et al.
ISBN: 9781401268329 | Diamond Code: AUG168504
Price: $16.99/$22.99 CAN | Format: TP

BATMAN ETERNAL VOL. 1

In the wake of FOREVER EVIL, the world looks at heroes in a different light, creating tension between Batman, his allies and the Gotham City Police Department.

Writers: Scott Snyder, Tim Seeley, James Tynion IV, Ray Fawkes & Kyle Higgins | Artists: Jason Fabok, et al.
ISBN: 978-1-4012-5173-4 | Diamond Code: SEP140302
Price: $39.99/$47.99 CAN | Format: TP

ALSO AVAILABLE: BATMAN ETERNAL VOL. 2-3

REBIRTH

BATMAN VOL. 1: I AM GOTHAM

Batman is back in an all-new series from rising star Tom King! The Dark Knight Detective must save Gotham from its newest threat...another vigilante hero!

Writer: Tom King | Artists: David Finch & Mikel Janin
ISBN: 9781401267773 | Diamond Code: OCT160291
Price: $16.99/$22.99 CAN | Format: TP

REBIRTH

DETECTIVE COMICS VOL. 1: THE RISE OF THE BATMEN

Gotham needs more than just the Bat. First cousins Batman and Batwoman pair up to train new and familiar vigilante recruits in the fight against an army of mysterious foes!

Writer: James Tynion IV
Artists: Eddy Barrows & Alvaro Martinez
ISBN: 9781401267995 | Diamond Code: NOV160317
Price: $16.99/$22.99 CAN | Format: TP

REBIRTH

BATMAN: NIGHT OF THE MONSTER MEN

The first crossover event of the Rebirth Era is here! As a huge storm approaches, Batman, Batwoman and Nightwing try to prepare Gotham for the worst, but nothing can prepare them for the monsters to come.

Writers: Tom King & Steve Orlando | Artist: Riley Rossmo
ISBN: 9781401270674 | Diamond Code: NOV160321
Price: $24.99/$33.99 CAN | Format: HC

REBIRTH

ALL-STAR BATMAN VOL. 1: MY OWN WORST ENEMY

The #1 *New York Times* best-selling author of BATMAN, Scott Snyder returns to the Dark Knight, this time with legendary artist John Romita Jr., as Two-Face unleashes his greatest attack ever.

Writer: Scott Snyder | Artists: John Romita Jr. & Declan Shalvey | ISBN: 9781401269784
Diamond Code: JUN160203 | Price: $24.99/$33.99 CAN
Format: HC | Coming April 25, 2017

READ THESE STAND-ALONE BATMAN GRAPHIC NOVELS

BATMAN: EARTH ONE VOL. 1

Geoff Johns reimagines the Dark Knight's origin story in this #1 *New York Times* bestseller.

Writer: Geoff Johns | Artist: Gary Frank
ISBN: 978-1-4012-3209-2 | Diamond Code: JUL158202
Price: $14.99/$17.99 CAN | Format: TP

BATMAN: EARTH ONE VOL. 2

Writer Geoff Johns and artist Gary Frank continue their astonishing new take on the Dark Knight as the Riddler attacks Gotham City.

Writer: Geoff Johns | Artist: Gary Frank
ISBN: 978-1-4012-6251-8 | Diamond Code: MAR160257
Price: $14.99/$17.99 CAN | Format: TP

THE DARK KNIGHT RETURNS: THE LAST CRUSADE

The prequel tale to one of the greatest graphic novels ever written, with art from the legendary John Romita Jr.

Writers: Frank Miller & Brian Azzarello | Artist: John Romita Jr.
ISBN: 9781401265069 | Diamond Code: AUG160319
Price: $17.99/$23.99 CAN | Format: HC

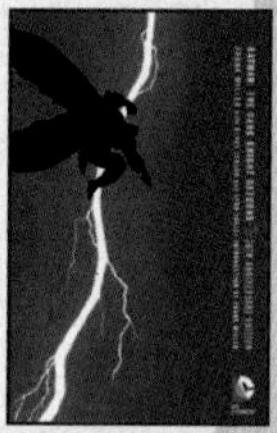

BATMAN: THE DARK KNIGHT RETURNS

Frank Miller's classic and gritty take on the return of Gotham's hero.

Writer: Frank Miller | Artist: Frank Miller
ISBN: 978-1-4012-6311-9 | Diamond Code: NOV150279
Price: $19.99/$23.99 CAN | Format: TP

BATMAN: THE DARK KNIGHT STRIKES AGAIN

The sequel to BATMAN: THE DARK KNIGHT RETURNS, in which Batman must come back once more to save a rapidly decaying world.

Writer: Frank Miller | Artist: Frank Miller
ISBN: 978-1-5638-9929-4 | Diamond Code: FEB058404
Price: $19.99/$23.99 CAN | Format: TP

DARK KNIGHT III: THE MASTER RACE

The highly anticipated third installment of Frank Miller's futuristic saga, co-written by Brian Azzarello (100 BULLETS) and illustrated by Andy Kubert (FLASHPOINT)!

Writers: Frank Miller & Brian Azzarello
Artists: Andy Kubert, Klaus Janson, Frank Miller, et al.
ISBN: 9781401265137 | Price: $29.99/$39.99 CAN
Format: HC | Coming Late 2017

EXPLORE ALL CORNERS OF GOTHAM WITH THESE GRAPHIC NOVELS!

BATGIRL VOL. 1: THE BATGIRL OF BURNSIDE

It's a reinvention of Batgirl from the boots up, by the incredible creative team of Cameron Stewart, Brenden Fletcher and rising star Babs Tarr.

Writers: Cameron Stewart & Brenden Fletcher
Artist: Babs Tarr
ISBN: 978-1-4012-5798-9 | Diamond Code: DEC148636
Price: $14.99/$17.99 CAN | Format: TP

ALSO AVAILABLE: BATGIRL VOL. 2-3

GRAYSON VOL. 1: AGENTS OF SPYRAL

Faking his own death, Dick Grayson becomes a super-spy as part of the clandestine organization Spyral.

Writers: Tim Seeley & Tom King | Artist: Mikel Janin
ISBN: 978-1-4012-5759-0 | Diamond Code: OCT150253
Price: $14.99/$17.99 CAN | Format: TP

ALSO AVAILABLE: GRAYSON VOL. 2-5

REBIRTH

BATGIRL VOL. 1: BEYOND BURNSIDE

Barbara Gordon (a.k.a. Batgirl) is leaving Burnside and hitting the road to find herself. Eisner winners Hope Larson and Raphael Albuquerque pair up to usher in a new era for beloved Babs.

Writer: Hope Larson | Artist: Rafael Albuquerque
ISBN: 9781401268404 | Diamond Code: TK
Price: $16.99/$22.99 CAN | Format: TP

REBIRTH

NIGHTWING VOL. 1: BETTER THAN BATMAN

Nightwing is back! Boy Wonder turned vigilante turned super-spy Dick Grayson returns to take down the international Parliament of Owls!

Writer: Tim Seeley | Artist: Javier Fernandez
ISBN: 9781401268039 | Diamond Code: OCT160296
Price: $16.99/$22.99 CAN | Format: TP

REBIRTH

BATGIRL AND THE BIRDS OF PREY VOL. 1: WHO IS ORACLE?

Batgirl, Black Canary and Huntress reunite to hunt down Gotham's all-seeing enemy, who goes by a familiar name: Oracle!

Writers: Shawna Benson & Julie Benson
Artist: Claire Roe | ISBN: 9781401268671 | Diamond Code: MAY160212 | Price: $16.99/$22.99 CAN | Format: TP | Coming April 25, 2017

REBIRTH

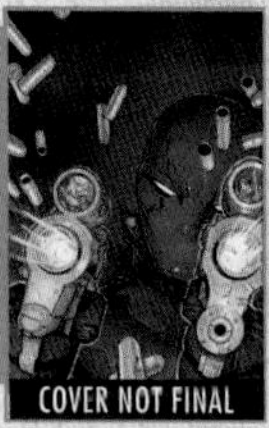

RED HOOD & THE OUTLAWS VOL. 1: DARK TRINITY

Red Hood embraces his bad side and looks to take down the crime lord Black Mask with the help of his new Outsiders: Bizarro and Artemis.

Writer: Scott Lobdell | Artist: Dexter Soy
ISBN: 9781401268756 | Diamond Code: TK
Price: $16.99/$22.99 CAN | Format: TP | Coming May 2, 2017

NIGHTWING VOL. 1: TRAPS AND TRAPEZES

Dick Grayson, once Batman's sidekick Robin, has grown up and become the high-flying Nightwing. Every bit the hero as his Caped Crusader mentor, he pursues justice on his own path.

Writer: Kyle Higgins | Artist: Eddy Barrows
ISBN: 978-1-4012-3705-9 | Diamond Code: JUL120214
Price: $14.99/$17.99 CAN | Format: TP

ALSO AVAILABLE: NIGHTWING VOL. 2-5

SUPERMAN

Since his earth-shattering debut in 1938's ACTION COMICS #1, Superman has achieved mythic folk hero status. Rocketed to Earth from the dying planet Krypton, baby Kal-El was raised on Earth by a kind-hearted farming couple. Clark Kent, as he was renamed, discovered that he had extraordinary and unmatched powers. Combining these abilities with the strong moral values his adoptive parents instilled in him, he became Superman. The Man of Steel soon became one of the most recognized and popular superheroes in all of pop culture, pushing past the printed page and emerging as an icon in all forms of media.

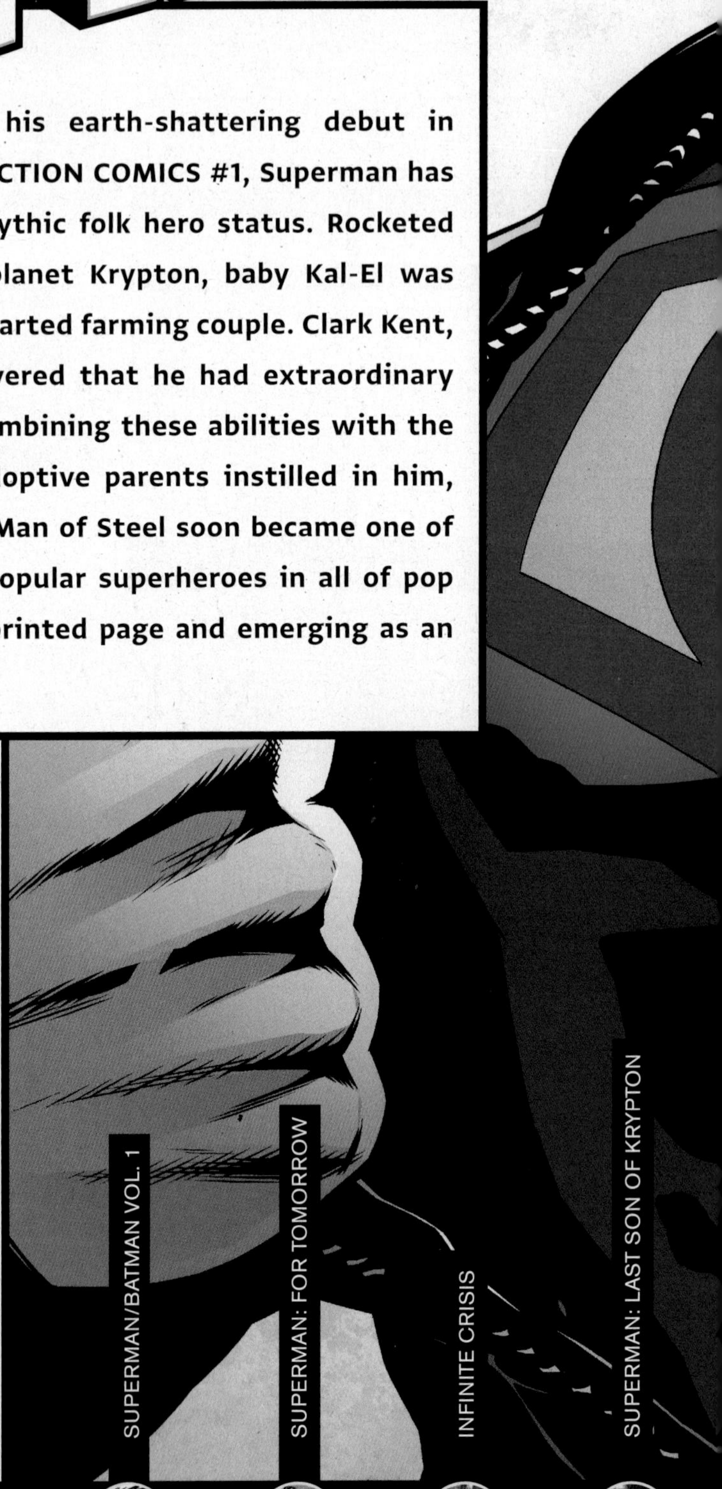

SUPERMAN: THE GOLDEN AGE VOL. 1

SUPERMAN: FOR ALL SEASONS

SUPERMAN: THE DEATH OF SUPERMAN

SUPERMAN/BATMAN VOL. 1

SUPERMAN: FOR TOMORROW

INFINITE CRISIS

SUPERMAN: LAST SON OF KRYPTON

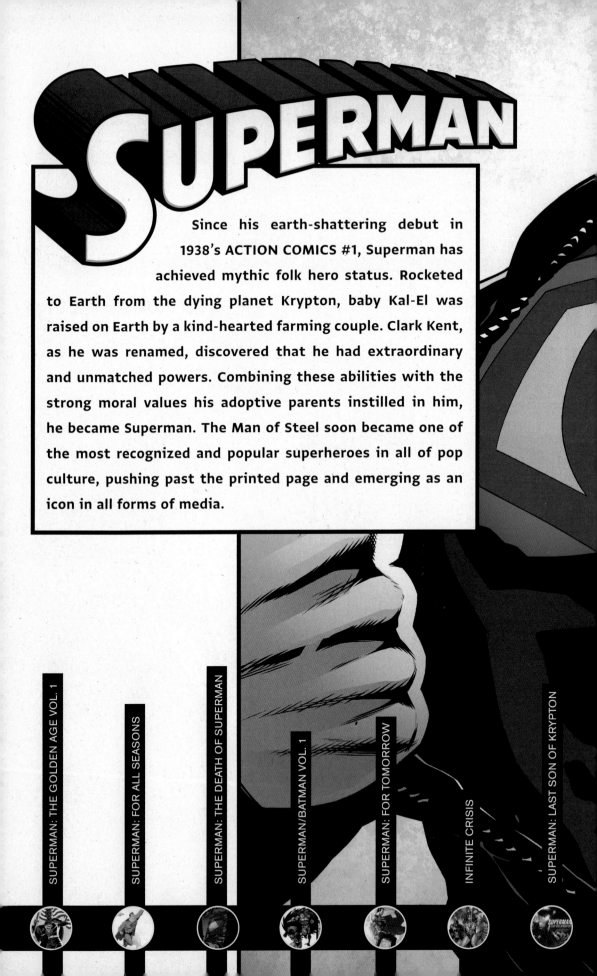

FLASHPOINT
SUPERMAN: THE MEN OF TOMORROW
SUPERMAN VOL. 1: BEFORE TRUTH
SUPERMAN: LOIS & CLARK
SUPERMAN: THE FINAL DAYS OF SUPERMAN
SUPERMAN: REBIRTH

SUPERMAN: THE GOLDEN AGE VOL. 1

Back to where it all began: Superman's very first, historic stories are now collected in one place, including the Man of Tomorrow's origin story and first battles against evil!

Writers: Jerry Siegel & Joe Shuster | Artists: Various
ISBN: 978-1-4012-6109-2 | Diamond Code: DEC150348
Price: $19.99/$23.99 CAN | Format: TP

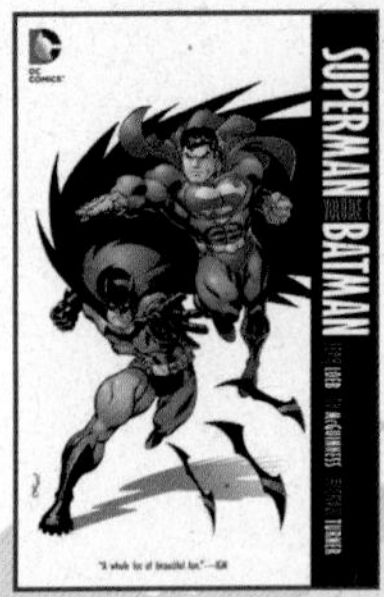

SUPERMAN/BATMAN VOL. 1

The iconic superheroes must unite to stop longtime Superman enemy Lex Luthor in this team-up tale from superstar writer Jeph Loeb (BATMAN: THE LONG HALLOWEEN).

Writer: Jeph Loeb | Artists: Ed McGuinness & Michael Turner
ISBN: 978-1-4012-4818-5 | Diamond Code: JAN140354
Price: $19.99/$23.99 CAN | Format: TP

SUPERMAN: FOR ALL SEASONS

The tale of Clark Kent's transformation from country boy to Metropolis Superman as told by the acclaimed duo of Jeph Loeb and Tim Sale.

Writer: Jeph Loeb | Artist: Tim Sale
ISBN: 978-1-5638-9529-6 | Diamond Code: FEB068194
Price: $17.99/$20.99 CAN | Format: TP

LUTHOR

The all-star team of Brian Azzarello and Lee Bermejo explores the mind of Superman's greatest villain, Lex Luthor.

Writer: Brian Azzarello | Artist: Lee Bermejo
ISBN: 978-1-4012-5818-4 | Diamond Code: AUG150269
Price: $14.99/$17.99 | Format: TP

SUPERMAN VOL.1: THE DEATH OF SUPERMAN

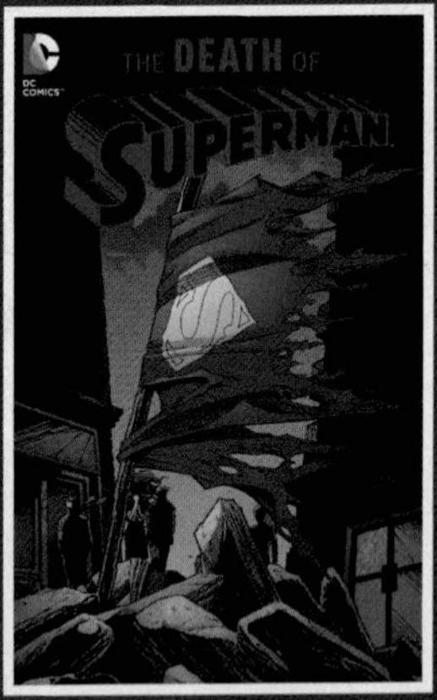

The story that shocked the world! Superman pays the ultimate price to stop the killing machine Doomsday.

Writers: Dan Jurgens, Jerry Ordway, Louise Simonson & Roger Stern | Artists: Dan Jurgens, Jon Bogdanove, Tom Grummett & Jackson Guice
ISBN: 9781401266653 | Diamond Code: JAN168880
Price: $17.99/$21.99 CAN | Format: TP

SUPERMAN FOR TOMORROW

A cataclysmic event has made half the Earth's population disappear, and no one is left unaffected, including Superman, in this graphic novel by the superstar team of Jim Lee and Brian Azzarello.

Writer: Brian Azzarello | Artist: Jim Lee
ISBN: 978-1-4012-3780-6 | Diamond Code: NOV120270
Price: $24.99/$28.99 CAN | Format: TP

SUPERMAN: LAST SON OF KRYPTON

Film director Richard Donner and Geoff Johns pit the Man of Steel against General Zod and Brainiac in these stories illustrated by Adam Kubert and Gary Frank.

Writers: Geoff Johns & Richard Donner | Artists: Adam Kubert & Gary Frank | ISBN: 978-1-4012-3779-0
Diamond Code: OCT120270
Price: $19.99/$23.99 CAN | Format: TP

BATMAN/SUPERMAN VOL. 1: CROSS WORLD

Discover how two of the World's Finest Superheroes met for the first time in the New 52 in this ultimate team-up.

Writer: Greg Pak | Artists: Jae Lee & Ben Oliver
ISBN: 978-1-4012-4934-2 | Diamond Code: AUG140333
Price: $14.99/$17.99 CAN | Format: TP

ALSO AVAILABLE: BATMAN/SUPERMAN VOL. 2-6

SUPERMAN VOL.1: BEFORE TRUTH

Gene Luen Yang, the National Book of the Year nominee and author of *American Born Chinese*, joins John Romita Jr. as Superman's identity is revealed to the world!

Writer: Gene Luen Yang | Artist: John Romita Jr.
ISBN: 978-1-4012-6510-6 | Diamond Code: JUN160356
Price: $16.99/$19.99 CAN | Format: TP

SUPERMAN UNCHAINED

All-star creators Scott Snyder and Jim Lee unite for the first time to take on the Man of Steel in this graphic novel blockbuster!

Writer: Scott Snyder | Artists: Jim Lee & Dustin Nguyen
ISBN: 978-1-4012-5093-5 | Diamond Code: DEC150346
Price: $24.99/$29.99 CAN | Format: TP

ROAD TO REBIRTH

SUPERMAN: LOIS AND CLARK

From the world before FLASHPOINT, the Man of Steel and the tough-as-nails reporter find themselves and their young son, Jonathan, on a new Earth. But in a harsh world that needs saving, is it time for Superman to reveal himself?

Writer: Dan Jurgens | Artist: Lee Weeks
ISBN: 978-1-4012-6249-5 | Diamond Code: MAY160323
Price: $17.99/$21.99 CAN CAN | Format: TP

SUPERMAN: THE MEN OF TOMORROW

Comics legends Geoff Johns and John Romita Jr. team up to launch an all-new era of Superman!

Writer: Geoff Johns | Artist: John Romita Jr.
ISBN: 978-1-4012-5868-9 | Diamond Code: JAN160315
Price: $16.99/$19.99 CAN | Format: TP

ROAD TO REBIRTH

SUPERMAN: THE FINAL DAYS OF SUPERMAN

It's a new chapter in the Man of Steel's life that will change everything you know about Superman, as the superhero faces his own last moments.

Writer: Peter J. Tomasi | Artists: Various
ISBN: 978-1-4012-6722-3 | Diamond Code: JUN160354
Price: $29.99/$39.99 CAN | Format: HC

REBIRTH

SUPERMAN – ACTION COMICS VOL. 1: PATH OF DOOM

Following the events of DC Rebirth, a new beginning includes an unlikely figure as the protector of Metropolis: Lex Luthor!

Writer: Dan Jurgens | Artists: Patrick Zircher & Tyler Kirkham
ISBN: 978-1-4012-6804-6 | Diamond Code: NOV160319
Price: $16.99/$22.99 CAN | Format: TP

REBIRTH

SUPERMAN VOL. 1: SON OF SUPERMAN

A new Superman appears to protect the world while raising a super-son with his wife, Lois Lane.

Writers: Peter J. Tomasi & Patrick Gleason
Artists: Patrick Gleason & Doug Mahnke
ISBN: 978-1-5638-9596-8 | Diamond Code: OCT160297
Price: $16.99/$22.99 CAN | Format: TP

REBIRTH

TRINITY VOL.1: BETTER TOGETHER

COVER NOT FINAL

New York Times best-selling creator Francis Manapul unites Batman, Superman, and Wonder Woman to protect the planet from threats too big for just one superhero.

Writer: Francis Manapul | Artists: Francis Manapul & Clay Mann | ISBN: 978-1-4012-7076-6
Price: $24.99/$33.99 CAN | Format: HC
Coming June 13, 2017

READ THESE STAND-ALONE SUPERMAN GRAPHIC NOVELS

SUPERMAN: EARTH ONE VOL. 1

The #1 *New York Times* best-selling original graphic novel that re-imagines Superman as a brooding, reluctant hero in modern-day Metropolis.

Writer: J. Michael Straczynski | Artist: Shane Davis
ISBN: 978-1-4012-2469-1 | Diamond Code: FEB130226
Price: $14.99/$19.99 CAN | Format: TP

ALSO AVAILABLE: SUPERMAN: EARTH ONE VOL. 2-3

SUPERMAN: AMERICAN ALIEN

A #1 *New York Times* bestseller! Hollywood screenwriter and Eisner Award nominee Max Landis joins forces with top comics illustrators to create a new epic that chronicles the life of Clark Kent.

Writer: Max Landis
Artists: Francis Manapul, Jae Lee, Nick Dragotta, Jock, et al.
ISBN: 978-1-4012-6256-3 | Diamond Code: JUN160357
Price: $24.99/ $29.99 | Format: HC

SUPERMAN: BIRTHRIGHT

Superstar writer Mark Waid updates the origin of the Man of Steel in this classic tale.

Writer: Mark Waid | Artist: Leinil Francis Yu
ISBN: 978-1-4012-0252-1 | Diamond Code: JUL050214
Price: $19.99/$23.99 CAN | Format: TP

SUPERMAN: RED SON

In this alternate take on the Man of Steel's origin, the ship carrying the infant who would grow up to become Superman lands in the midst of 1950s Soviet Union.

Writer: Mark Millar | Artists: Dave Johnson & Killian Plunkett
ISBN: 978-1-4012-4711-9 | Diamond Code: JAN140353
Price: $17.99/$20.99 CAN | Format: TP

ALL-STAR SUPERMAN

The critically acclaimed series that harkens back to the Golden Age of Superman by superstar writer Grant Morrison and artist Frank Quitely.

Writer: Grant Morrison | Artist: Frank Quitely
ISBN: 978-1-4012-3205-4 | Diamond Code: JUL110247
Price: $29.99/$35.00 CAN | Format: TP

CHECK OUT THE ADVENTURES OF THE MAN OF STEEL'S ALLIES

SUPERGIRL VOL. 1
LAST DAUGHTER OF KRYPTON

Superman's teenage cousin mysteriously crash-lands on Earth decades after the destruction of Krypton.

Writers: Michael Green & Mike Johnson | Artist: Mahmud Asrar
ISBN: 978-1-4012-3680-9 | Diamond Code: JUL120216
Price: $14.99/$17.99 CAN | Format: TP

ALSO AVAILABLE: SUPERGIRL VOL. 2-6

REBIRTH

COVER NOT FINAL

SUPERWOMAN VOL. 1
WHO KILLED SUPERWOMAN?

The newly super-powered Lois Lane must take on the task of being the protector of Metropolis. The only problem is, her newfound powers are killing her!

Writer: Phil Jimenez | Artist: Phil Jimenez
ISBN: 978-1-4012-6780-3 | Price: $16.99/$22.99 CAN
Format: TP | Coming May 9, 2017

REBIRTH

COVER NOT FINAL

SUPERGIRL VOL. 1
REIGN OF THE CYBORG SUPERMEN

Supergirl moves to National City in this new series that's perfect for fans of the hit TV show, now on the CW.

Writer: Steve Orlando | Artist: Brian Ching
ISBN: 978-1-4012-6846-6 | Price: $16.99/$22.99 CAN
Format: TP | Coming May 2, 2017

REBIRTH

COVER NOT FINAL

NEW SUPER-MAN VOL. 1:
MADE IN CHINA

The #1 *New York Times* best-selling author Gene Luen Yang introduces a new Man of Steel, created by the Chinese government. But the government may have chosen the wrong person for the job.

Writer: Gene Luen Yang | Artist: Viktor Bogdanovic
ISBN: 978-1-4012-7093-3 | Price: $16.99/$22.99 CAN
Format: TP | Coming June 27, 2017

WONDER WOMAN

Celebrate more than 75 years of the most recognizable superheroine of all time: Wonder Woman. An essential figure in the DC Universe, Wonder Woman has been a symbol of empowerment through seven formative decades. With a jubilee this year, as well as the release of the highly anticipated feature film *Wonder Woman*, 2017 is the year of the Amazon Princess. She is Diana, princess of the immortal Amazons from Greek mythology, equipped with powers granted by the gods of Olympus and an arsenal of iconic weapons, from her Lasso of Truth to her indestructible Bracelets of Submission. Since her first appearance in 1941, Wonder Woman has been unparalleled in brains, beauty and brawn—a warrior princess beyond worthy of her status as a pop culture icon.

WONDER WOMAN 75

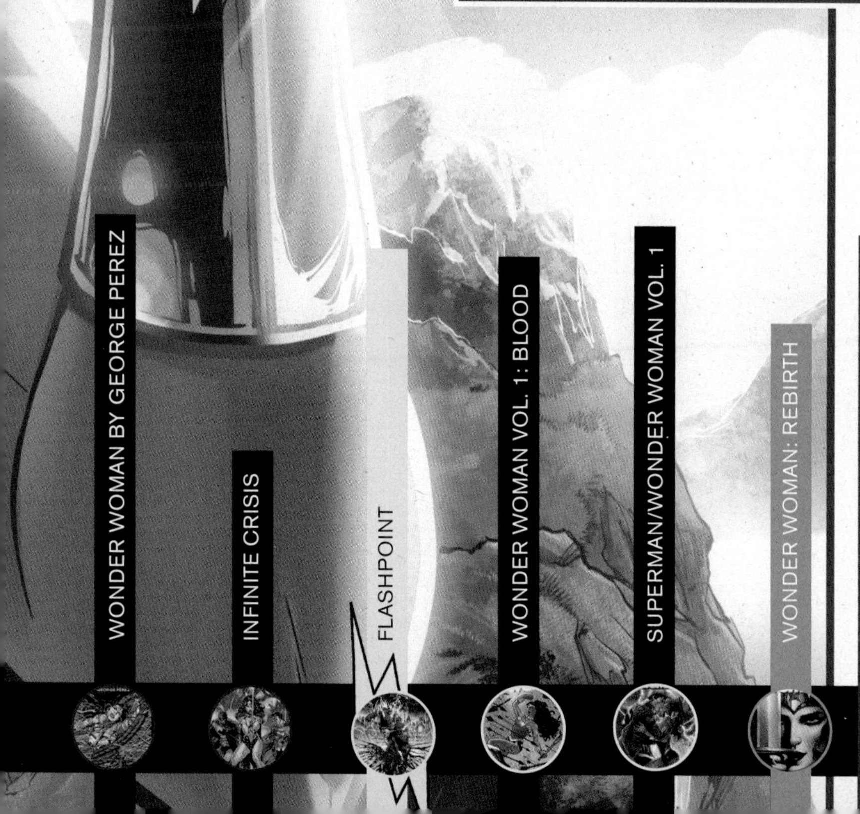

WONDER WOMAN: A CELEBRATION OF 75 YEARS

This anthology collects Wonder Woman's greatest stories throughout seven decades as one of the DC Universe's greatest heroes.

Writers: Various | Artists: Various
ISBN: 978-1-4012-6206-8 | Diamond Code: MAY160330
Price: $39.99/$43.99 CAN | Format: HC

WONDER WOMAN: HER GREATEST BATTLES

This ultimate companion collection for 2017's highly anticipated film *Wonder Woman* features the biggest and best stories from the greatest talents in comics to ever work with the Amazon Princess.

Writer: Various | Artist: Various
ISBN: 978-1-4012-6375-1 | Diamond Code: MAY160328
Price: $9.99/$13.50 CAN | Format: TP

WONDER WOMAN BY GEORGE PÉREZ VOL. 1

This anthology collects Wonder Woman's greatest stories throughout seven decades as one of the DC Universe's greatest heroes.

Writer: George Perez | Artist: George Pérez
ISBN: 978-1-4012-6206-8 | Diamond Code: MAY160330
Price: $24.99/$29.99 CAN | Format: TP

WONDER WOMAN BY GREG RUCKA VOL. 1

Greg Rucka's first and now legendary run on the Amazon Warrior begins as Diana is the new Themysciran ambassador to the United Nations.

Writer: Greg Rucka | Artist: Various
ISBN: 978-1-4012-6332-4 | Diamond Code: APR160406
Price: $29.99/$35.99 CAN | Format: TP

WONDER WOMAN VOL. 1: BLOOD

Superheroics meet ancient myth as critically acclaimed writer Brian Azzarello teams with Cliff Chiang and Tony Akins to begin a new chapter for the Amazon Princess.

Writer: Brian Azzarello | Artists: Cliff Chiang & Tony Akins
ISBN: 978-1-4012-3562-8 | Diamond Code: OCT120256
Price: $14.99/$17.99 CAN | Format: TP

SUPERMAN/WONDER WOMAN VOL. 1: POWER COUPLE

The greatest superhero couple in the universe sets off on their own adventures! The creature that once killed the Man of Steel returns to finish him—but will the combined might of Superman and Wonder Woman be enough to eliminate this overpowering threat?

Writer: Charles Soule | Artist: Tony S. Daniel
ISBN: 978-1-4012-5346-2 | Diamond Code: DEC140383
Price: $16.99/$19.99 CAN | Format: TP

REBIRTH

WONDER WOMAN VOL. 1 THE LIES

New York Times best-selling writer Greg Rucka returns to Wonder Woman with a tale that will forever alter the DC icon.

Writer: Greg Rucka | Artist: Liam Sharp
ISBN: 978-1-4012-6778-0 | Price: $16.99/$22.99 CAN
Format: TP

READ THESE STAND-ALONE WONDER WOMAN GRAPHIC NOVELS

WONDER WOMAN: THE TRUE AMAZON

In this original graphic novel of Wonder Woman from writer/artist Jill Thompson (*The Little Endless Storybook*), a spoiled young princess, Diana—the future Wonder Woman—must learn to take responsibility for her actions.

Writer: Jill Thompson | Artist: Jill Thompson
ISBN: 978-1-4012-4901-4 | Diamond Code: MAY160281
Price: $22.99/$29.99 CAN | Format: HC

THE LEGEND OF WONDER WOMAN

This unique new retelling of Wonder Woman's origin follows a young Diana as she learns the lessons that will eventually help her become the Amazon Warrior!

Writer: Renae De Liz | Artist: Renae De Liz
ISBN: 978-1-4012-6728-5 | Diamond Code: AUG160332
Price: $29.99/$39.99 CAN | Format: HC

WONDER WOMAN: EARTH ONE VOL. 1

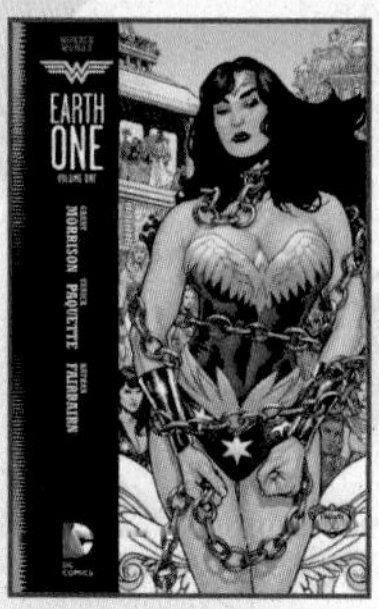

Comics masters Grant Morrison and Yanick Paquette continue the best-selling Earth One series with a provocative take on Wonder Woman for the modern world.

Writer: Grant Morrison | Artist: Yanick Paquette
ISBN: 978-1-4012-6863-3 Price: $16.99/$22.99 CAN
Format: TP

WONDER WOMAN '77 VOL. 1

Experience the adventures of Lynda Carter's Wonder Woman as this series continues the stories inspired by the 1977 hit TV show.

Writer: Marc Andreyko | Artists: Various
ISBN: 978-1-4012-6328-7 | Diamond Code: MAR160277
Price: $16.99/$19.99 CAN | Format: TP

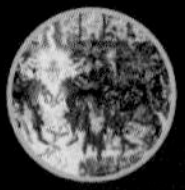
CRISIS ON INFINITE EARTHS

JLA VOL. 1

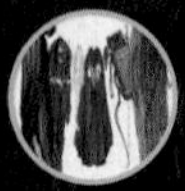
IDENTITY CRISIS

INFINITE CRISIS

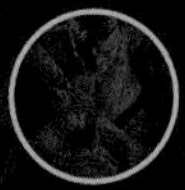
FINAL CRISIS

FLASHPOINT

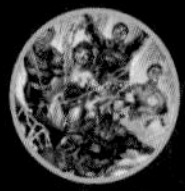
JUSTICE LEAGUE VOL. 1: ORIGIN

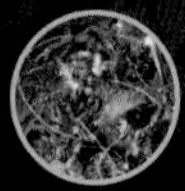
THRONE OF ATLANTIS

JUSTICE LEAGUE: TRINITY WAR

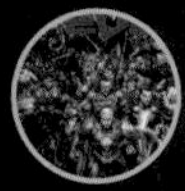
FOREVER EVIL

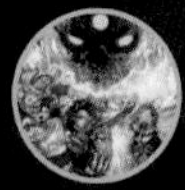
CONVERGENCE

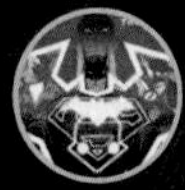
JUSTICE LEAGUE: DARKSEID WAR

JUSTICE LEAGUE: REBIRTH

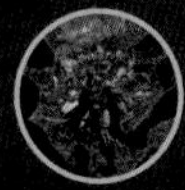
JUSTICE LEAGUE VS. SUICIDE SQUAD

Greater than the sum of their awe-inspiring parts, the Justice League handles threats too massive for any single hero, and 2017 will see the whole team starring in their own feature film. Made up of the World's Greatest Super Heroes, the core lineup is known as the Big Seven: Superman, Batman, Wonder Woman, the Flash, Green Lantern, Aquaman and Cyborg. These graphic novels featuring this super-team stand out as not only great JUSTICE LEAGUE reads, but as some of the most important works in DC history.

JUSTICE
LEAGUE

JUSTICE LEAGUE OF AMERICA: THE SILVER AGE VOL. 1

For the first time, JLA's first 20 adventures are collected in a single volume, spanning 1960-1964.

Writers: Various | Artists: Various
ISBN: 978-1-4012-6111-5 | Diamond Code: NOV150283
Price: $19.99/$23.99 CAN | Format: TP

CRISIS ON INFINITE EARTHS

Worlds will live and worlds will die in comics' original epic event storyline by the legendary creative team of Marv Wolfman and George Pérez.

Writer: Marv Wolfman | Artist: George Pérez
ISBN: 978-1-5638-9750-4 | Diamond Code: AUG058162
Price: $29.99/$35.00 CAN | Format: TP

JLA VOL. 1

Grant Morrison relaunches the greatest team in the DC Universe—returning the powerhouse lineup of Superman, Batman, Wonder Woman, the Flash, Green Lantern, Aquaman and Martian Manhunter!

Writer: Grant Morrison | Artist: Howard Porter
ISBN: 978-1-4012-3314-3 | Diamond Code: JUN110276
Price: $19.99/$23.99 CAN | Format: TP

ALSO AVAILABLE: JLA VOL. 2-9

INFINITE CRISIS

It's the DCU's darkest day, and long-lost heroes from the past return to make things right in this epic sequel to CRISIS ON INFINITE EARTHS.

Writer: Geoff Johns | Artists: Phil Jimenez, Jerry Ordway & George Pérez | ISBN: 978-1-4012-1060-1
Diamond Code: FEB118149 | Price: $17.99/$20.99 | Format: TP

IDENTITY CRISIS

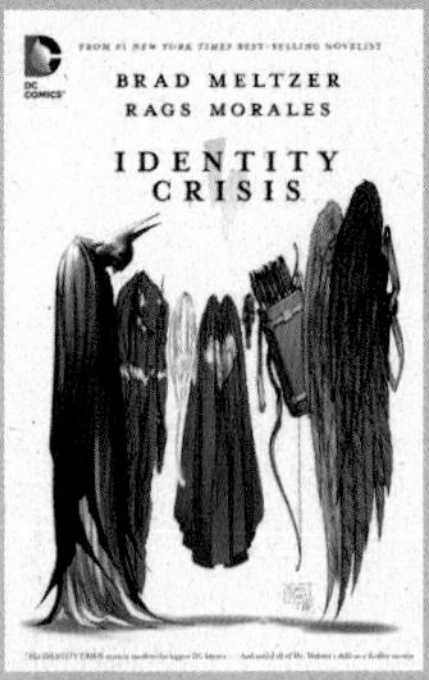

Uncover the DC Universe's deadliest secret in this acclaimed miniseries from *New York Times* best-selling novelist Brad Meltzer.

Writer: Brad Meltzer | Artist: Rags Morales
ISBN: 978-1-4012-6313-3 | Diamond Code: TK
Price: $19.99/$23.99 CAN | Format: TP

FINAL CRISIS

Grant Morrison takes the DC Universe on a battle through the Multiverse that will leave both hero and villain changed forever.

Writer: Grant Morrison | Artists: J.G. Jones, Doug Mahnke & Carlos Pacheco | ISBN: 978-1-4012-4517-7
Diamond Code: JAN140352 | Price: $19.99/$23.99 CAN | Format: TP

JUSTICE LEAGUE VOL. 1: ORIGIN

In one of the most game-changing titles in comics industry history, Geoff Johns and Jim Lee reimagine the Justice League for the 21st century.

Writer: Geoff Johns | Artist: Jim Lee
ISBN: 978-1-4012-3788-2 | Diamond Code: OCT120252
Price: $16.99/$19.99 CAN | Format: TP

JUSTICE LEAGUE VOL. 3:
THRONE OF ATLANTIS

The armies of Atlantis attack the surface world pitting the Justice League against one of their own.

Writer: Geoff Johns | Artists: Ivan Reis & Tony S. Daniel
ISBN: 978-1-4012-4698-3 | Diamond Code: JAN140339
Price: $16.99/$19.99 CAN | Format: TP

JUSTICE LEAGUE VOL. 6:
INJUSTICE LEAGUE

The Justice League roster you've never seen before, all led by the world's greatest hero—Lex Luthor!

Writer: Geoff Johns | Artists: Doug Mahnke & Jason Fabok
ISBN: 978-1-4012-5852-8 | Diamond Code: DEC150328
Price: $19.99/$23.99 CAN | Format: TP

JUSTICE LEAGUE:
TRINITY WAR

When the three Justice Leagues go to war with one another, whose side will everyone be on? Allies will be born, friends will become enemies, and the DC Universe will never be the same.

Writers: Geoff Johns & Jeff Lemire | Artists: Ivan Reis, Doug Mahnke & Mikel Janin | ISBN: 978-1-4012-4944-1
Diamond Code: AUG140331 | Price: $19.99/$23.99 | Format: TP

CONVERGENCE

Every DC Universe from the past, present and future collide here in this mega-event that will change the course of every story ever told in DC Comics history.

Writers: Jeff King & Scott Lobdell | Artists: Carlo Pagulayan & Stephen Segovia | ISBN: 978-1-4012-6487-1
Diamond Code: JUL160401 | Price: $24.99/$29.99 CAN | Format: TP

FOREVER EVIL

The Justice League is dead! An evil version of the Justice League takes over the DC Universe, and no one stands in the way... no one except for Lex Luthor.

Writer: Geoff Johns | Artist: David Finch
ISBN: 978-1-4012-5338-7 | Diamond Code: FEB150254
Price: $19.99/$23.99 CAN | Format: TP

JUSTICE LEAGUE VOL. 5:
FOREVER HEROES

New York Times best-selling writer Geoff Johns continues the FOREVER EVIL event, as the Justice League must find a way to defeat their deadly mirror images—the Crime Syndicate!

Writer: Geoff Johns | Artists: Ivan Reis & Doug Mahnke
ISBN: 978-1-4012-5419-3 | Diamond Code: DEC140382
Price: $14.99/$17.99 CAN | Format: TP

JUSTICE LEAGUE VOL. 7:
DARKSEID WAR PART 1

Darkseid and the Anti-Monitor—two of the most powerful beings in the universe—face off in one of the biggest Justice League storylines ever!

Writer: Geoff Johns | Artist: Jason Fabok
ISBN: 978-1-4012-6452-9 | Diamond Code: JUN160346
Price $16.99/$22.99 CAN | Format: TP

JUSTICE LEAGUE VOL. 8: DARKSEID WAR PART 2

The conclusion to Geoff Johns' critically acclaimed best-selling run on the World's Greatest Heroes.

Writer: Geoff Johns | Artists: Jason Fabok & Francis Manapul
ISBN: 978-1-4012-6539-7 | Diamond Code: MAY160312
Price: $16.99/$22.99 CAN | Format: TP

JUSTICE LEAGUE VOL. 8: DARKSEID WAR—POWER OF THE GODS

Spinning off of Geoff Johns' epic Darkseid War, the members of the Justice League inherit the powers of the gods!

Writers: Tom King, Peter J. Tomasi, Francis Manapul & Steve Orlando | Artists: Various
ISBN: 978-1-4012-5976-1 | Diamond Code: APR150167
Price: $24.99/$29.99 CAN | Format: HC

REBIRTH

JUSTICE LEAGUE VOL. 1: THE EXTINCTION MACHINES

Following DC Rebirth, the World's Greatest Superheroes—the Justice League—come together again to face new, more devastating threats!

Writer: Bryan Hitch | Artist: Tony S. Daniel
ISBN: 978-1-4012-6779-7 | Diamond Code: OCT160295
Price: $16.99/$22.99 CAN | Format: TP

REBIRTH

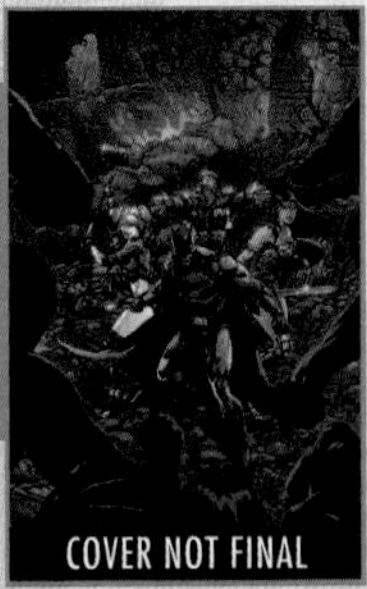

JUSTICE LEAGUE /SUICIDE SQUAD

Two of the DC Universe's most powerful super-teams square off in this event graphic novel, written by Steve Orlando and rising star Joshua Williamson.

Writers: Joshua Williamson & Steve Orlando | Artists: Various
ISBN: 978-1-4012-7226-5 | Price: $39.99/$53.99 CAN | Format: HC
Coming June 27, 2017

FOLLOW THE ADVENTURES OF THE MEMBERS OF THE JUSTICE LEAGUE!

AQUAMAN VOL. 1: THE TRENCH

Superstar writer Geoff Johns reteams with artist Ivan Reis to relaunch Aquaman as one of the most powerful and important heroes of the DC Universe.

Writer: Geoff Johns | Artist: Ivan Reis
ISBN: 978-1-4012-3710-3 | Diamond Code: FEB130206
Price: $14.99/$17.99 CAN | Format: TP

ALSO AVAILABLE: AQUAMAN VOL. 2-8

REBIRTH

AQUAMAN VOL. 1: THE DROWNING

A new era for the king of Atlantis begins as Aquaman attempts to broker peace between Atlantis and the surface world, while Black Manta launches his most lethal strike ever against his arch-foe!

Writer: Dan Abnett | Artists: Brad Walker & Philippe Briones
ISBN: 978-1-4012-6782-7 | Diamond Code: OCT160290
Price: $16.99/$22.99 CAN | Format: TP

REBIRTH

CYBORG VOL. 1: THE IMITATION OF LIFE

Justice League member Cyborg, in his own series, begins his greatest quest to date: to find his soul...if he has one!

Writer: John Semper Jr.
Artists: Will Conrad & Paul Pelletier | ISBN: 9781401267926
Price: $16.99/$22.99 CAN | Format: TP

GREEN ARROW BY JEFF LEMIRE & ANDREA SORRENTINO DELUXE EDITION

Green Arrow had finally found a sense of purpose, friends to aid him and even a place on the Justice League of America. Now he's not even sure where he came from...or *who* he came from.

Writer: Jeff Lemire | Artist: Andrea Sorrentino
ISBN: 978-1-4012-5761-3 | Diamond Code: AUG150271
Price: $49.99/$58.00 CAN | Format: HC

REBIRTH

GREEN ARROW VOL. 1: THE DEATH & LIFE OF OLIVER QUEEN

Oliver Queen is back in Seattle to uncover an illegal human-trafficking operation when he comes face-to-face with a familiar yet mysterious love—Black Canary!

Writer: Benjamin Percy | Artists: Otto Schmidt & Juan Ferreyra | ISBN: 978-1-4012-6781-0 | Diamond Code: OCT160293
Price: $16.99/$22.99 CAN | Format: TP

SHAZAM! VOL. 1

By shouting a wizard's name—Shazam!—young teen Billy Batson is mystically transformed into the powerhouse known as Captain Marvel.

Writer: Geoff Johns | Artist: Gary Frank
ISBN: 978-1-4012-4699-0 | Diamond Code: FEB140251
Price: $16.99/$19.99 CAN | Format: TP

The Flash

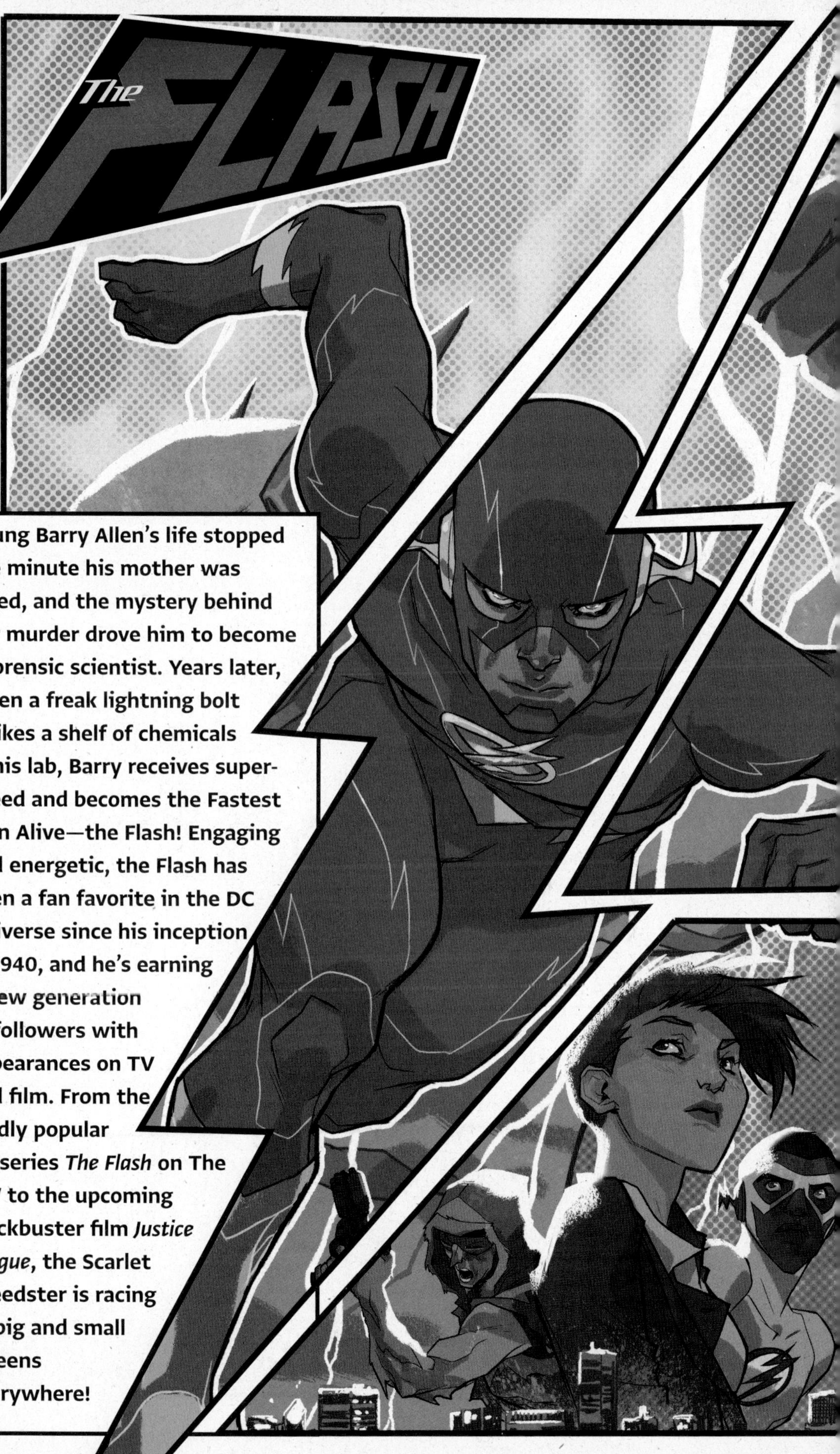

Young Barry Allen's life stopped the minute his mother was killed, and the mystery behind her murder drove him to become a forensic scientist. Years later, when a freak lightning bolt strikes a shelf of chemicals in his lab, Barry receives super-speed and becomes the Fastest Man Alive—the Flash! Engaging and energetic, the Flash has been a fan favorite in the DC Universe since his inception in 1940, and he's earning a new generation of followers with appearances on TV and film. From the wildly popular TV series *The Flash* on The CW to the upcoming blockbuster film *Justice League*, the Scarlet Speedster is racing to big and small screens everywhere!

THE FLASH BY GEOFF JOHNS BOOK ONE

The critically acclaimed and best-selling adventures of Wally West, the Fastest Man Alive, as written by Geoff Johns.

Writer: Geoff Johns | Artist: Scott Kolins
ISBN: 978-1-4012-5873-3 | Diamond Code: AUG150268
Price: $24.99/$29.99 CAN | Format: AUG150268

THE FLASH VOL. 1: MOVE FORWARD

The Fastest Man Alive returns as Central City's greatest protector.

Writers: Francis Manapul & Brian Buccellato
Artist: Francis Manapul | ISBN: 978-1-4012-3554-3
Diamond Code: MAY130224 | Price: $16.99/$19.99 CAN
Format: TP

ALSO AVAILABLE: THE FLASH VOL. 2-9

THE FLASH: REBIRTH

The explosive epic that reintroduces the newly returned Barry Allen as the Flash!

Writer: Geoff Johns | Artist: Ethan Van Sciver
ISBN: 978-1-4012-3001-2 | Diamond Code: JAN110329
Price: $14.99/$17.99 CAN | Format: TP

FLASHPOINT

Heroes become villains in an alternate-universe tale that changed the DC Universe forever!

Writer: Geoff Johns | Artist: Andy Kubert
ISBN: 978-1-4012-3338-9| Diamond Code: OCT138324
Price: $16.99/$19.99 CAN | Format: TP

REBIRTH

THE FLASH VOL. 1: LIGHTNING STRIKES TWICE

Rising star writer Joshua Williamson heralds in a new era for the Flash, who finds himself in a city of speedsters after a familiar lightning storm.

Writer: Joshua Williamson
Artists: Carmine Di Giandomenico & Neil Googe
ISBN: 978-1-4012-6784-1 | Diamond Code: OCT160292
Price: $17.99/$23.99 CAN | Format: TP

When a dying alien crashes on Earth, reckless test pilot Hal Jordan is chosen to be its successor in the universal peacekeeping force known as the Green Lantern Corps. Armed with a power ring that has the ability to create anything he can imagine, the newest Green Lantern faces his greatest fears and the most dangerous villains in the universe. With a varied group of heroes such as Jessica Cruz, Simon Baz, Guy Gardner and John Stewart aiding Hal's cause, these graphic novels are among the most diverse from DC.

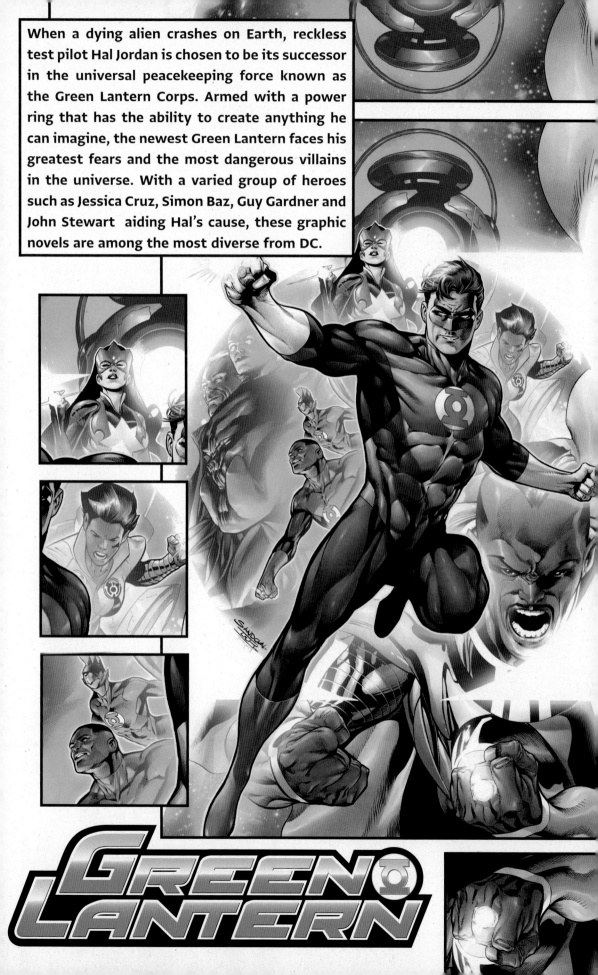

GREEN LANTERN: THE SILVER AGE VOL. 1

At last, the first Silver Age adventures of Green Lantern are available in a massive, colorful paperback.

Writers: Various | Artists: Various
ISBN: 978-1-4012-6348-5 | Diamond Code: JUL160410
Price: $24.99/$33.99 | Format: TP

GREEN LANTERN: REBIRTH

A jaw-dropping epic that reintroduces the quintessential Green Lantern, Hal Jordan!

Writer: Geoff Johns | Artist: Ethan Van Sciver
ISBN: 978-1-4012-2953-5 | Diamond Code: APR110192
Price: $19.99/$23.99 CAN | Format: TP

GREEN LANTERN: SECRET ORIGIN

Witness the beginnings of the greatest Green Lantern of all in this graphic novel.

Writer: Geoff Johns | Artist: Ivan Reis
ISBN: 978-1-4012-3086-9 | Diamond Code: JAN110337
Price: $14.99/$17.99 CAN | Format: TP

BLACKEST NIGHT

Hal Jordan and the Green Lantern Corps lead DC's champions into battle to save the universe from an army of undead Black Lanterns!

Writer: Geoff Johns | Artist: Ivan Reis
ISBN: 978-1-4012-2953-5 | Diamond Code: APR110192
Price: $19.99/$23.99 CAN | Format: TP

GREEN LANTERN VOL. 1: SINESTRO

Hal Jordan has been stripped of his ring. And an unexpected new Green Lantern is left in town: Sinestro!

Writer: Geoff Johns | Artist: Doug Mahnke
ISBN: 978-1-4012-3455-3 | Diamond Code: OCT120257
Price: $14.99/$17.99 CAN | Format: TP

SINESTRO VOL. 1: THE DEMON WITHIN

The deadliest villain in the Green Lantern mythos gets his own series for the first time!

Writer: Cullen Bunn | Artist: Dale Eaglesham
ISBN: 978-1-4012-5050-8 | Diamond Code: OCT140359
Price: $14.99/$17.99 CAN | Format: TP

GREEN LANTERN CORPS: EDGE OF OBLIVION VOL. 1

The Green Lantern Corps is lost in space and now the universe is dying around them.

Writer: Tom Taylor | Artist: Ethan Van Sciver
ISBN: 978-1-4012-6550-2 | Diamond Code: AUG160329
Price: $16.99/$22.99 CAN | Format: TP

REBIRTH

GREEN LANTERNS VOL. 1: RAGE PLANET

Rookie Green Lanterns Jessica Cruz and Simon Baz must overcome their clashing personalities and tackle the universe's toughest beat: Earth!

Writer: Sam Humphries | Artist: Robson Rocha
ISBN: 978-1-4012-6775-9 | Diamond Code: TK
Price: $17.99/$23.99 CAN | Format: TP

REBIRTH

HAL JORDAN & THE GREEN LANTERN CORPS VOL. 1: SINESTRO'S LAW

Robert Venditti launches a new era as Hal Jordan and the Corps must rise up against the new force of justice in the universe: the Sinestro Corps!

Writer: Robert Venditti | Artists: Ethan Van Sciver & Rafa Sandoval
ISBN: 978-1-4012-6800-8 | Diamond Code: TK
Price: $16.99/$22.99 CAN | Format: TP

Harley Quinn, Deadshot, Killer Croc, Captain Boomerang, El Diablo and the Enchantress—six of the deadliest and most unpredictable metahumans on the planet are finally being put to good use. Government agent Amanda Waller has sanctioned them to be part of Task Force X, led by Rick Flag and Katana, in which these villainous prisoners will complete dangerous missions in exchange for freedom. Conceptualized in 1959 and revived in modern form by John Ostrander in 1987, the Suicide Squad are the stars of the blockbuster film from DC.

SUICIDE SQUAD VOL. 1: KICKED IN THE TEETH

Former super-villains are recruited by a shadowy government agency for missions so dangerous, it's suicide.

Writer: Adam Glass | Artists: Federico Dallocchio & Clayton Henry | ISBN: 978-1-4012-3544-4
Diamond Code: APR120250 | Price: $14.99/$17.99 CAN
Format: TP

ALSO AVAILABLE: SUICIDE SQUAD VOL. 2-5

HARLEY QUINN VOL. 1: HOT IN THE CITY

The Cupid of Crime returns in her smash-hit solo series! Jimmy Palmiotti and Amanda Conner unleash Harley on an unsuspecting DC Universe, leaving no one unscathed in her wake.

Writers: Jimmy Palmiotti & Amanda Conner | Artist: Chad Hardin
ISBN: 978-1-4012-5415-5 | Diamond Code: JAN150369
Price: $16.99/$19.99 CAN | Format: TP

NEW SUICIDE SQUAD VOL. 1: PURE INSANITY

Deadshot. Harley Quinn. The Joker's Daughter. Black Manta. Deathstroke. The world's most dangerous incarcerated super-villains are sent to carry out impossible missions on foreign soil in exchange for a commuted prison sentence.

Writer: Sean Ryan | Artist: Sean Ryan
ISBN: 978-1-4012-5238-0 | Diamond Code: APR150302
Price: $16.99/$19.99 | Format: TP

HARLEY QUINN AND HER GANG OF HARLEYS

What's better than one Harley? Well, quite frankly, we'd prefer none, but this will have to do. This strange new army of Harleys will have to rescue the kidnapped original in this wacky new series!

Writers: Jimmy Palmiotti & Frank Tieri
Artist: Mauricet | ISBN: 978-1-4012-6785-8
Price: $16.99/$22.99 CAN | Format: TP

REBIRTH

SUICIDE SQUAD VOL. 1: THE BLACK VAULT

From Rob Williams, superstar artist Jim Lee and Philip Tan comes the new Suicide Squad—Harley Quinn, Deadshot, Captain Boomerang, Katana and Killer Croc!

Writer: Rob Williams | Artists: Jim Lee & Philip Tan
ISBN: 978-1-4012-6981-4 | Price: $16.99/$22.99 CAN
Format: TP| Coming March 7, 2017

HARLEY'S LITTLE BLACK BOOK

Finally! The team-up book that no one asked for! See what trouble Harley can get into when she joins forces with Superman, Wonder Woman, Green Lantern and some of the greatest heroes in the DC Universe.

Writers: Jimmy Palmiotti & Amanda Conner | Artist: Various
ISBN: 978-1-4012-6976-0
Price: $24.99/$33.99 CAN | Format: HC | Coming April 11, 2017

BATMAN: THE KILLING JOKE

The definitive Joker origin story from the mind of legendary writer Alan Moore.

Writer: Alan Moore | Artist: Brian Bolland
ISBN: 978-1-4012-1667-2 | Diamond Code: NOV070226
Price: $17.99/$20.99 CAN | Format: HC | FOR MATURE READERS

REBIRTH

HARLEY QUINN VOL. 1: DIE LAUGHING

Jimmy Palmiotti and Amanda Conner spearhead Harley's return in the wake of DC Rebirth as her crazy world gets even crazier.

Writers: Jimmy Palmiotti & Amanda Conner
Artists: Chard Hardin & John Timms
ISBN: 978-1-4012-6831-2 | Diamond Code: TK
Price: $16.99/$22.99 CAN | Format: TP

FROM PAGE TO SCREEN

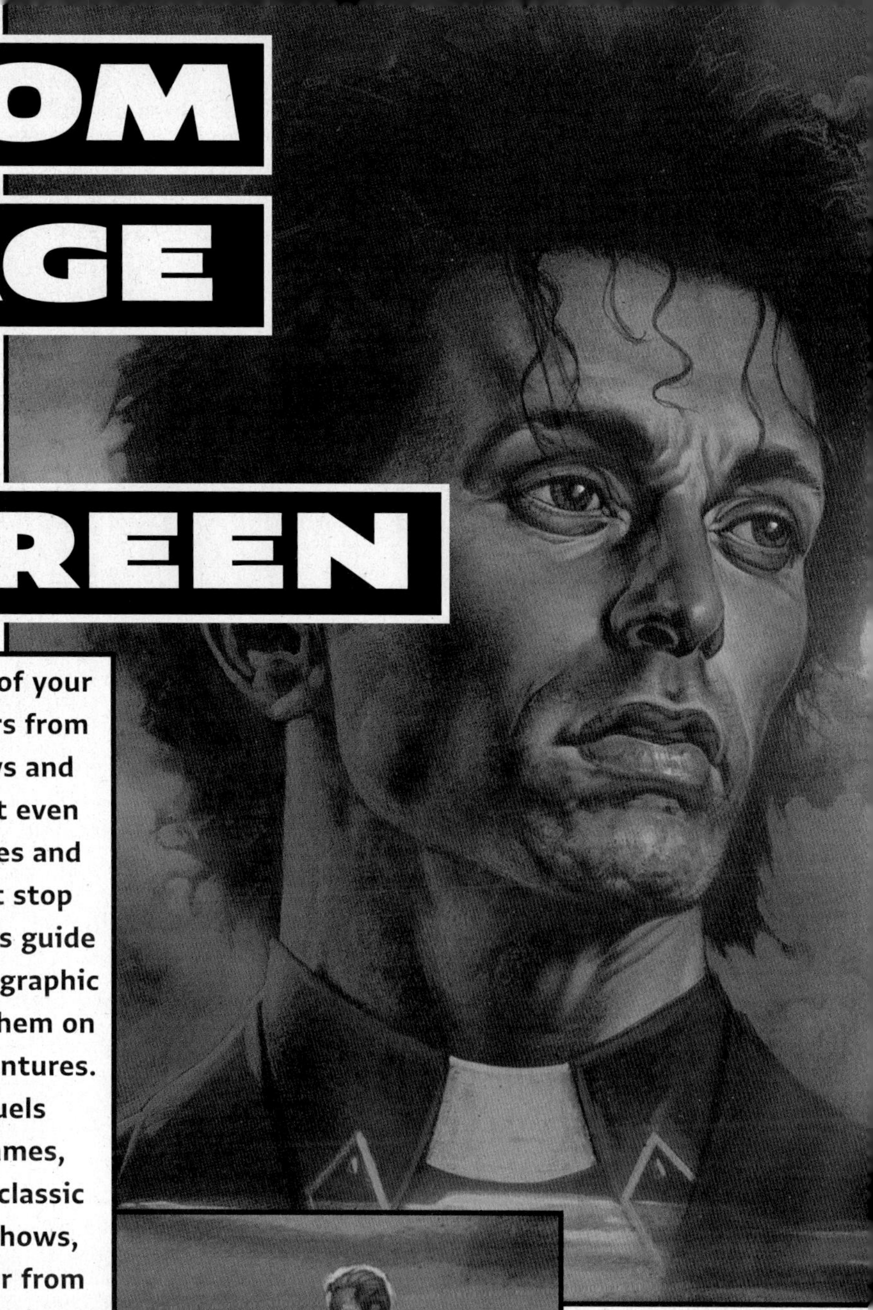

Can't get enough of your favorite characters from movies, TV shows and video games? Get even more of the heroes and villains you can't stop watching with this guide to the comics and graphic novels that take them on their wildest adventures. Between prequels and hit video games, continuations of classic and modern TV shows, storylines familiar from movies and more, there are plenty of ways to be a comics fan.

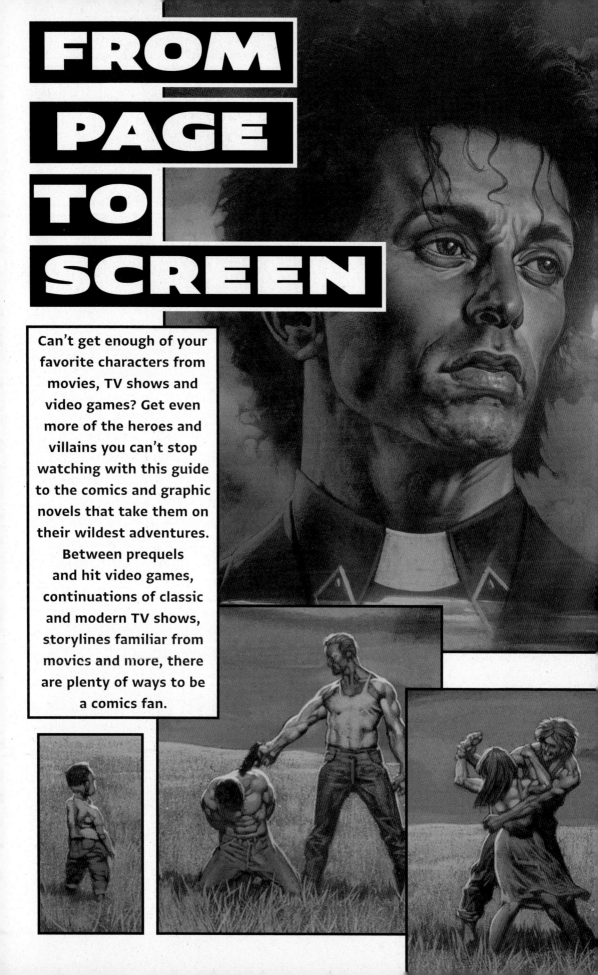

WONDER WOMAN: HER GREATEST BATTLES

Writers: Various | Artists: Various
ISBN: 978-1-4012-6897-8
Diamond Code: NOV160343
Price: $9.99/ $13.50 CAN
Format: TP

WONDER WOMAN BY GEORGE PÉREZ VOL. 1

Writer: George Peréz
Artists: George Peréz
ISBN: 978-1-4012-3810-0
Diamond Code: JUN130271
Price: $24.99/$29.99 CAN | Format: TP

After 75 years, the Amazon warrior finally gets her very own film in 2017! Starring Gal Gadot, WONDER WOMAN brings to life one of the most celebrated heroes ever to grace the printed page. Read these stories starring the characters and exotic locales of the highly anticipated movie!

WONDER WOMAN VOL. 1: THE LIES

Writer: Greg Rucka
Artist: Liam Sharp
ISBN: 978-1-4012-6778-0
Diamond Code: NOV160320
Price: $16.99/$22.99 CAN |
Format: TP

WONDER WOMAN: EARTH ONE VOL. 1

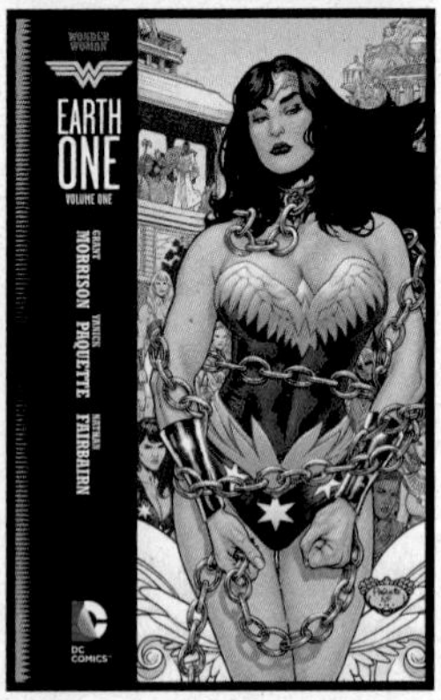

Writer: Grant Morrison
Artist: Yanick Paquette
ISBN: 978-1-4012-6863-3
Price: $16.99/ $22.99 CAN
Format: TP

WONDER WOMAN VOL. 1: BLOOD

Writer: Brian Azzarello
Artists: Cliff Chiang & Tony Akins
ISBN: 978-1-4012-3562-8
Diamond Code: OCT120256
Price: $14.99/$17.99 CAN
Format: TP

JUSTICE LEAGUE

FALL 2017

The World's Greatest Super Heroes finally get their own feature film in 2017. These graphic novels are prime examples of what makes JUSTICE LEAGUE one of the best reads in all of comics.

JUSTICE LEAGUE VOL. 1: ORIGIN

Writer: Geoff Johns | Artist: Jim Lee
ISBN: 978-1-4012-3788-2
Diamond Code: OCT120252
Price: $16.99/$19.99 CAN | Format: TP

JUSTICE LEAGUE: THEIR GREATEST TRIUMPHS

Writers: Various | Artists: Various
ISBN: 978-1-4012-7351-4
Price: $9.99/ $13.50 CAN
Format: TP

JUSTICE LEAGUE VOL. 1: THE EXTINCTION MACHINES

Writer: Bryan Hitch | Artist: Tony S. Daniel | ISBN: 978-1-4012-6779-7
Diamond Code: OCT160295
Price: $16.99/$22,99 CAN
Format: TP

SUPERMAN VOL. 1: SON OF SUPERMAN

Writers: Peter J. Tomasi & Patrick Gleason | Artists: Patrick Gleason & Doug Mahnke |
ISBN: 978-1-4012-6776-6 |
Diamond Code: OCT160297 | Price: $16.99/$22.99 CAN | Format: TP

BATMAN VOL. 1: THE COURT OF OWLS

Writer: Scott Snyder
Artist: Greg Capullo
ISBN: 978-1-4012-3542-0
Diamond Code: DEC120323
Price: $16.99/$19.99 CAN

BATMAN VOL. 1: I AM GOTHAM

Writer: Tom King
Artists: David Finch & Mikel Janin
ISBN: 978-1-4012-6777-3
Diamond Code: OCT160291
Price: $16.99/$22.99 CAN
Format: TP

WONDER WOMAN VOL. 1: BLOOD

Writer: Brian Azzarello
Artists: Cliff Chiang & Tony Akins
ISBN: 978-1-4012-3562-8
Diamond Code: OCT120256
Price: $14.99/$17.99 CAN
Format: TP

THE FLASH VOL. 1: MOVE FORWARD

Writers: Francis Manapul & Brian Buccellato | Artist: Francis Manapul
ISBN: 978-1-4012-3554-3
Diamond Code: MAY130224
Price: $16.99/$19.99 CAN
Format: TP

AQUAMAN VOL. 1: THE TRENCH

Writer: Geoff Johns
Artist: Ivan Reis
ISBN: 978-1-4012-3710-3
Diamond Code: FEB130206
Price: $14.99/$17.99 CAN
Format: TP

CYBORG VOL. 1: THE IMITATION OF LIFE

Writer: John Semper Jr.
Artists: Will Conrad & Paul Pelletier
ISBN: 978-1-4012-6792-6
Price: $16.99/$22.99 CAN
Format: TP

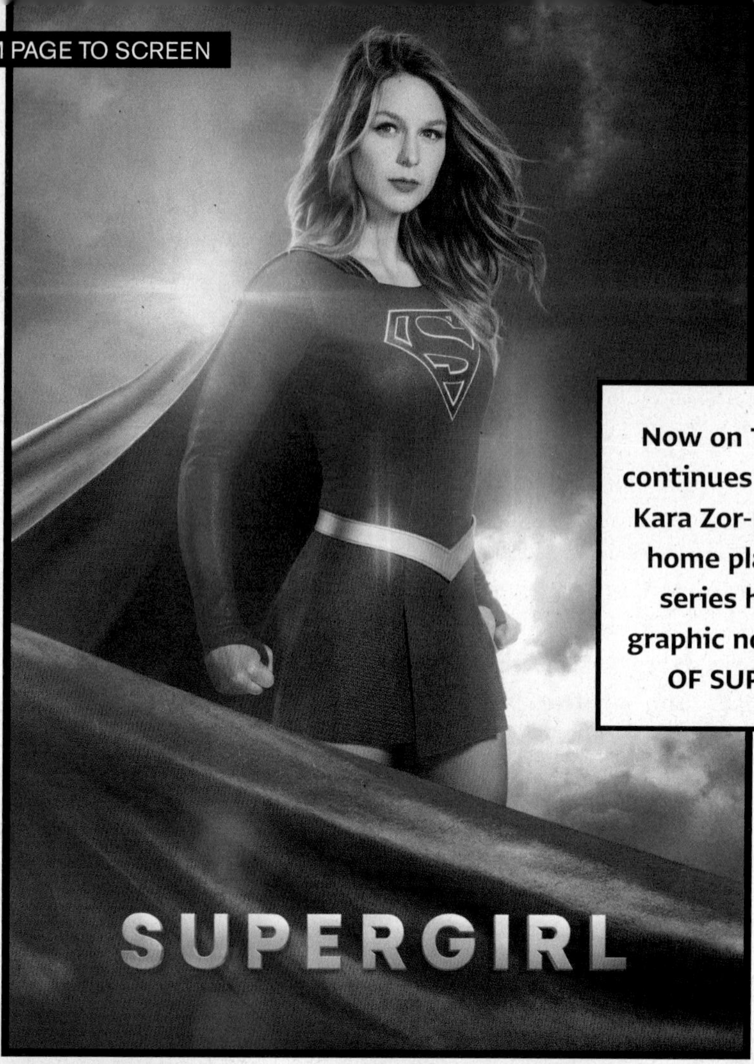

Now on The CW, *Supergirl* continues the adventures of Kara Zor-El on her adopted home planet, Earth. This series has inspired the graphic novel ADVENTURES OF SUPERGIRL VOL. 1!

SUPERGIRL VOL. 1:
LAST DAUGHTER OF KRYPTON

Writers: Michael Green & Mike Johnson | Artist: Mahmud Asrar
ISBN: 978-1-4012-3680-9
Diamond Code: JUL120216
Price: $14.99/$17.99 CAN
Format: TP

SUPERGIRL:
THE COMPLETE FIRST SEASON

DVD: SRP: $49.99 | UPC: 883929524389
BLU-RAY: SRP: $54.97 | UPC: 883929524396

ADVENTURES OF SUPERGIRL VOL. 1

Writer: Sterling Gates
Artists: Various
ISBN: 978-1-4012-6265-5
Diamond Code: APR160389
Price: $16.99/$22.99 CAN
Format: TP

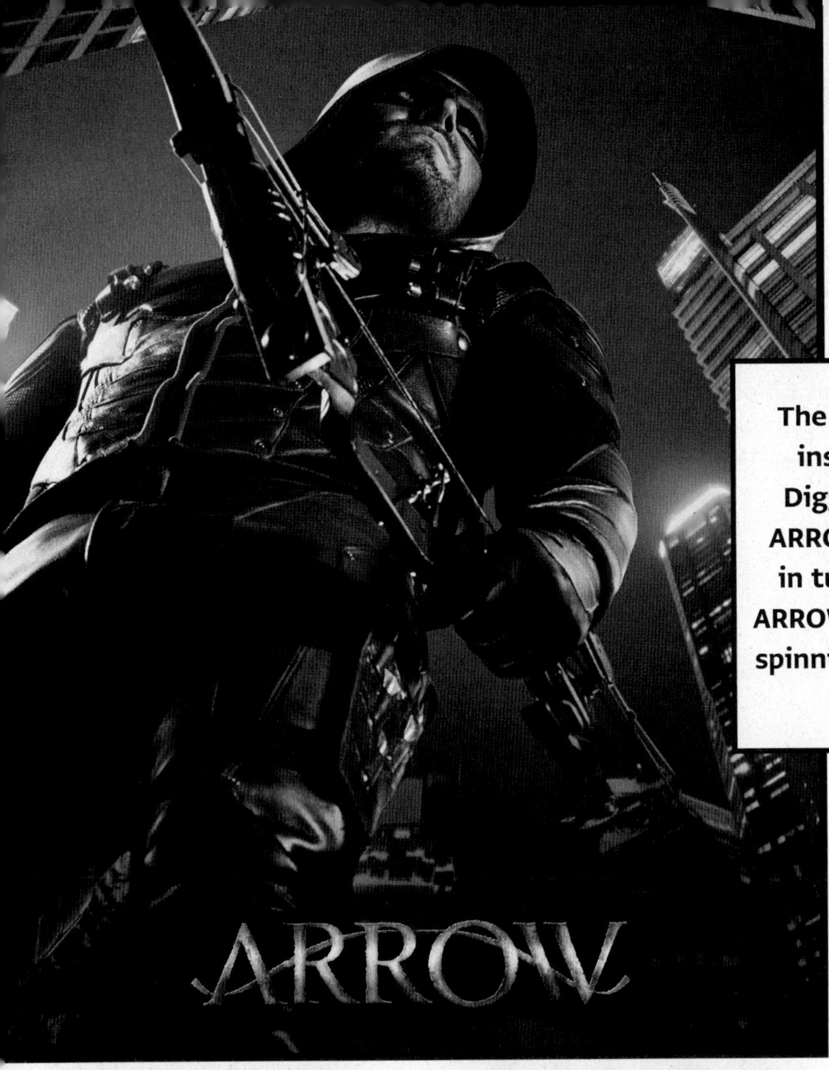

The CW's hit series drew inspiration from Andy Diggle and Jock's GREEN ARROW: YEAR ONE, which in turn helped create the ARROW VOL. 1 graphic novel, spinning off from the events of the show.

GREEN ARROW: YEAR ONE

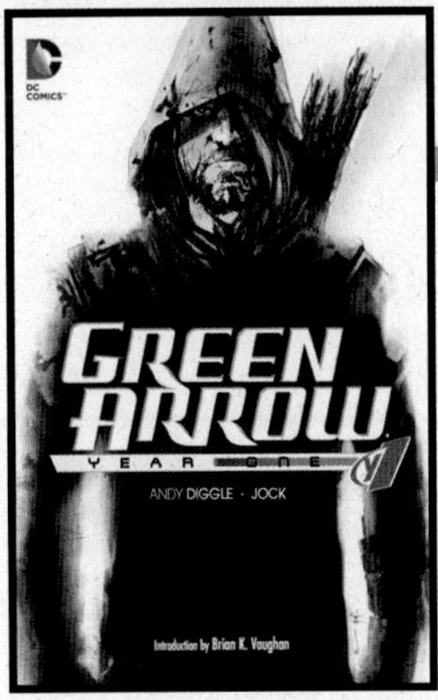

Writer: Andy Diggle | Artist: Jock
ISBN: 978-1-4012-1743-3
Diamond Code: JAN090227
Price: $14.99/$17.99 CAN
Format: TP

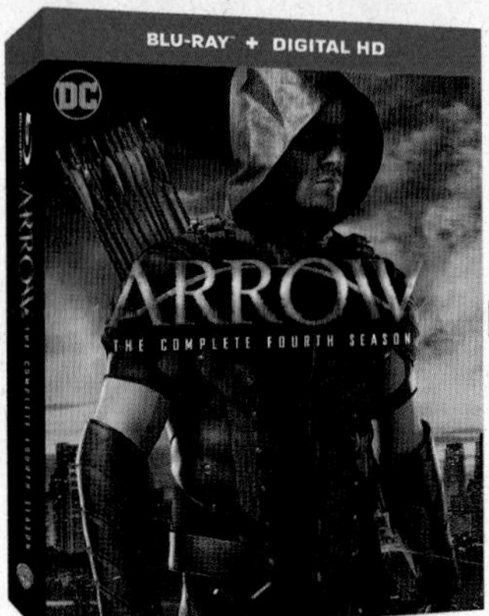

ARROW: THE COMPLETE FOURTH SEASON

DVD: SRP: $49.99 | UPC: 883929524112
BLU-RAY: SRP: $54.97 | UPC: 883929524129

ARROW VOL. 1

Writers: Marc Guggenheim & Andrew Kreisberg | Artist: Mike Grell | ISBN: 978-1-4012-4299-2
Diamond Code: JUN130265
Price: $16.99/$19.99 CAN
Format: TP

THE FLASH

THE FLASH continues to be one of the hottest shows on television, which has helped create the popular spin-off graphic novel THE FLASH: SEASON ZERO.

THE FLASH VOL. 1:
MOVE FORWARD

Writers: Francis Manapul & Brian Buccellato | Artist: Francis Manapul | ISBN: 978-1-4012-3554-3
Diamond Code: MAY130224
Price: $16.99/$19.99 CAN
Format: TP

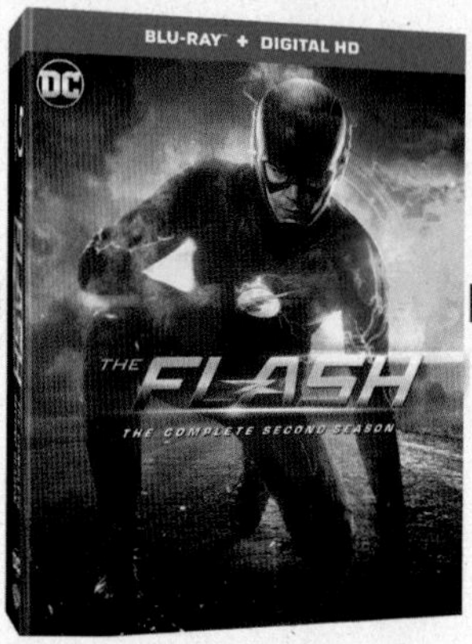

THE FLASH: THE COMPLETE SECOND SEASON

DVD: SRP: $49.99 | UPC: 883929524433
BLU-RAY: SRP: $54.97 | UPC: 883929524440

THE FLASH:
SEASON ZERO

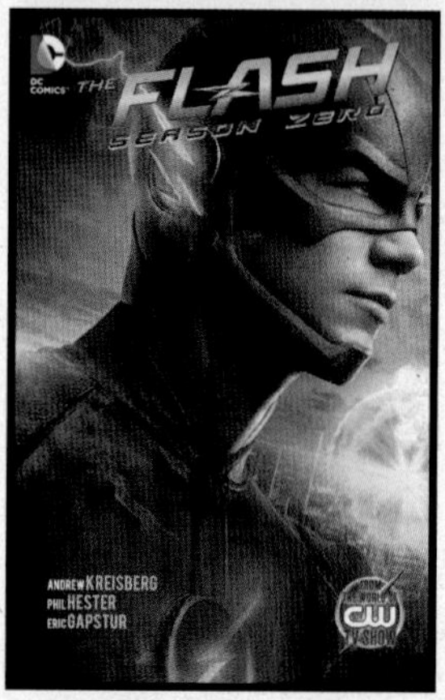

Writer: Andrew Kreisberg
Artists: Phil Hester & Marcus To
ISBN: 978-1-4012-5771-2
Diamond Code: JUN150297
Price: $19.99/$23.99 CAN
Format: TP

A cast of unexpected and unforgettable superheroes come together in The CW show *DC's Legends of Tomorrow*. Taking place in the same universe as hit shows *Arrow*, *Supergirl* and *The Flash*, recognizable heroes like Firestorm, the Atom and Hawkgirl are now brought to life in this hit series!

DC'S LEGENDS OF TOMORROW: THE COMPLETE FIRST SEASON

DVD: SRP: $39.99 | UPC: 883929524259
BLU-RAY: SRP: $44.98 | UPC: 883929524198

iZOMBIE

IZOMBIE VOL. 1:
DEAD TO THE WORLD

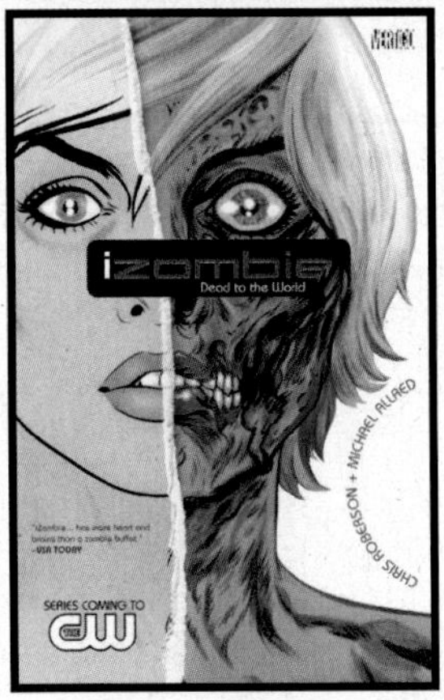

Writer: Chris Roberson
Artist: Mike Allred
ISBN: 978-1-4012-2965-8
Diamond Code: DEC100299
Price: $14.99/$17.99 CAN
Format: TP

IZOMBIE:
THE COMPLETE
SECOND SEASON

DVD: SRP: $39.99
UPC: 883929524518

Craving more of The CW's *iZombie*? Read about your favorite brain-eating gal with the entire iZOMBIE series from Vertigo.

THE CW

PREACHER BOOK ONE

Writer: Garth Ennis
Artist: Steve Dillon
ISBN: 978-1-4012-4045-5
Diamond Code: MAR130303
Price: $19.99/$23.99 CAN
Format: TP

PREACHER

One of the greatest Vertigo series of all time, from the creative team of Garth Ennis and Steve Dillon, is brought to the small screen in the dark and thrilling *Preacher* TV series on AMC.

PREACHER:
SEASON ONE

DVD: SRP: $45.99
UPC: 043396476622
BLU-RAY: SRP: $65.99
UPC: 043396476608

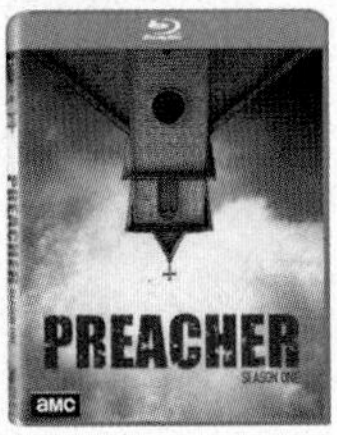

Go back to the beginning with rising detective Jim Gordon and the seedy underbelly of Gotham in these pivotal Batman origin stories, which directly inspire the heroes and villains of FOX's hit show *Gotham*.

BATMAN: YEAR ONE

Writer: Frank Miller | Artist: David Mazzucchelli | ISBN: 978-1-4012-0752-6
Diamond Code: OCT060163
Price: $14.99/$17.99 CAN | Format: TP

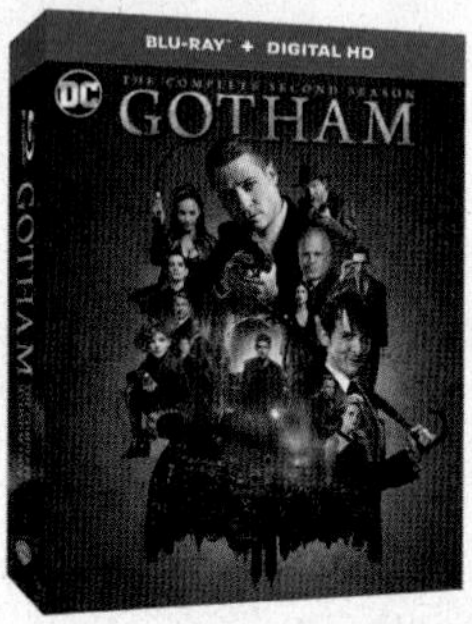

GOTHAM: THE COMPLETE SECOND SEASON

DVD: SRP: $49.99 | UPC: 883929524204
BLU-RAY: SRP: $54.97 | UPC: 883929524211

FOX

BATMAN: EARTH ONE

Writer: Geoff Johns| Artist: Gary Frank
ISBN: 978-1-4012-3209-2
Diamond Code: JUL158202
Price: $14.99/$17.99 CAN | Format: TP

LUCIFER BOOK ONE

Writer: Mike Carey
Artists: Peter Gross & Scott Hampton | ISBN: 978-1-4012-4026-4
Diamond Code: FEB130247
Price: $29.99/$35.00 CAN
Format: TP

LUCIFER:
THE COMPLETE
FIRST SEASON

DVD: SRP: $39.99
UPC: 883929546800

FOX

What happens when Satan gets bored of Hell? In FOX's *Lucifer*, the devil himself takes up residence in L.A., the City of Angels, charming women and getting everyone to spill their darkest truths. Get the whole story of the retired ruler of Hell in Vertigo's LUCIFER series.

INJUSTICE
GODS AMONG US

The video game phenomenon is back with a vengeance! Prepare yourself for INJUSTICE 2—coming in 2017—with the hit graphic novel series!

INJUSTICE:
GODS AMONG US YEAR ONE-
THE COMPLETE EDITION

Writer: Tom Taylor
Artists: Jheremy Raapack &
Mike S. Miller
ISBN: 978-1-4012-5798-9
Diamond Code: DEC150338
Price: $24.99/29.99 CAN | Format: TP

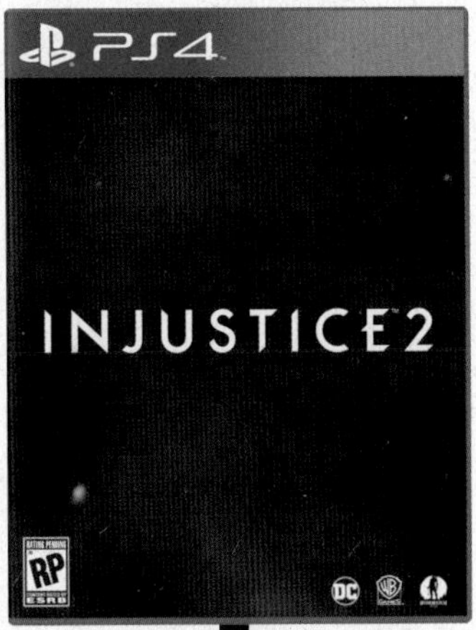

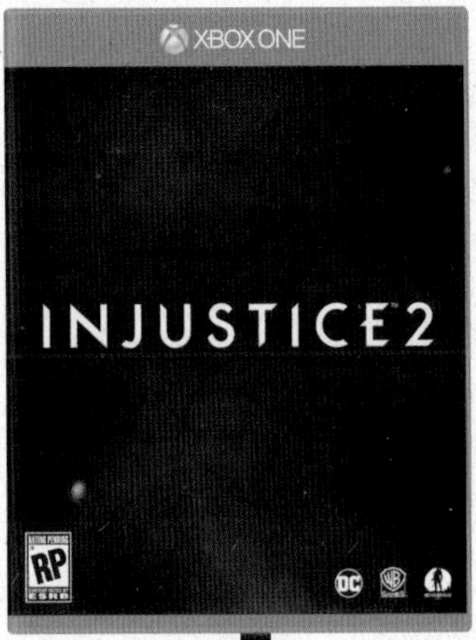

INJUSTICE 2
PS4: SRP: $59.99 | UPC: 883929552337
XONE: SRP: $59.99 | UPC: 883929552320

VERTIGO

ESSENTIAL GRAPHIC NOVELS

Through fantasy, nonfiction, horror and romance, Vertigo has created award-winning and critically acclaimed bestsellers for more than 20 years. Created for a mature audience, Vertigo's titles have pushed the limits of graphic storytelling, exploring uncharted territory with writers and artists who have emerged as industry legends. Enter the unexpected worlds of Vertigo's inimitable stories with some of the imprint's finest graphic novels.

100 BULLETS BOOK ONE

If guaranteed full immunity, what would you do? Vertigo's seminal crime series features ordinary citizens who are given the opportunity to exact revenge on a person who has wronged them.

Writer: Brian Azzarello | Artist: Eduardo Risso
ISBN: 978-1-4012-5056-0 | Diamond Code: JUL140274
Price: $24.99/$28.99 CAN | Format: TP

ALSO AVAILABLE: 100 BULLETS BOOKS TWO–FIVE

AMERICAN VAMPIRE VOL. 1

Scott Snyder and legendary novelist Stephen King offer a stirring take on the Vampire mythology.

Writers: Stephen King & Scott Snyder | Artist: Rafael Albuquerque
ISBN: 978-1-4012-2974-0 | Diamond Code: JUL110284
Price: $19.99/$23.99 CAN | Format: TP

ALSO AVAILABLE: AMERICAN VAMPIRE VOL. 2-9

DAYTRIPPER

This award-winning graphic novel follows Bras de Oliva Domingo during different periods in his life, each with the same ending: his death.

Writers: Gabriel Bá & Fábio Moon | Artists: Gabriel Bá & Fábio Moon
ISBN: 978-1-4012-2969-6 | Diamond Code: NOV100268
Price: $19.99/$23.99 CAN | Format: TP

DOOM PATROL BOOK ONE

Grant Morrison reinvents the Silver Age super-team as only he can, as the Doom Patrol investigates the surreal corners of the DC Universe.

Writer: Grant Morrison | Artist: Richard Case
ISBN: 978-1-4012-6312-6 | Diamond Code: NOV150304
Price: $24.99/$29.99 CAN | Format: TP

ALSO AVAILABLE: DOOM PATROL BOOKS TWO AND THREE

FABLES VOL. 1: LEGENDS IN EXILE

Folklore comes to life as these real-life fairy tale characters are exiled in modern-day New York City.

Writer: Bill Willingham | Artist: Lan Medina
ISBN: 978-1-4012-3755-4 | Diamond Code: FEB120285
Price: $12.99/$15.99 | Format: TP

ALSO AVAILABLE: FABLES VOL. 2-22

EVERAFTER: FROM THE PAGES OF FABLES VOL. 1

Spinning off of Bill Willingham's classic saga, this new graphic novel series details The Shadow Players, a secret agency tasked with policing a new enchanted planet Earth!

COVER NOT FINAL

Writers: Matthew Sturges & Dave Justus
Artist: Travis Moore | ISBN: 978-1-4012-6836-7
Price: $16.99/$22.99 | Format: TP | Coming May 9, 2017

GET JIRO!

The star of TV's *No Boundaries*, Anthony Bourdain slashes his way into comics with this outrageous action-adventure tale of katanas and sushi.

Writers: Anthony Bourdain & Joel Rose | Artist: Langdon Foss
ISBN: 978-1-4012-2828-6 | Diamond Code: FEB130242
Price: $14.99/$17.99 CAN | Format: TP

THE INVISIBLES BOOK ONE

Throughout history, a secret society called the Invisibles has worked against dark forces conspiring to end mankind.

Writer: Grant Morrison | Artists: Steve Yeowell & Jill Thompson
ISBN: 978-1-5638-9267-7 | Diamond Code: SEP068118
Price: $24.99/$33.99 CAN | Format: TP

ALSO AVAILABLE: THE INVISIBLES BOOKS TWO-FOUR

JOHN CONSTANTINE, HELLBLAZER VOL. 1: ORIGINAL SINS

In the longest-running Vertigo series ever, Earth's resident exorcist, demonologist and master of the dark arts, John Constantine, is on the side of the angels—but he's willing to make a deal with a demon to prevail.

Writer: Jamie Delano | Artists: John Ridgway, Alfredo Alcala, Rick Veitch & Tom Mandrake | ISBN: 978-1-4012-3006-7
Diamond Code: DEC100302 | Price: $19.99/$23.99 CAN | Format: TP

ALSO AVAILABLE: JOHN CONSTANTINE, HELLBLAZER VOL. 2-14

THE LEAGUE OF EXTRAORDINARY GENTLEMEN VOL. 1

The best-known characters of 19th century literature band together in Alan Moore's award-winning graphic novel.

Writer: Alan Moore | Artist: Kevin O'Neill
ISBN: 978-1-5638-9858-7 | Diamond Code: MAY118167
Price: $16.99/$19.99 CAN | Format: TP

LUCIFER BOOK ONE

In this inspiration behind the new Fox TV show, the king of Hell abdicates his throne for a life on Earth.

Writer: Mike Carey | Artists: Peter Gross & Scott Hampton
ISBN: 978-1-4012-4026-4 | Diamond Code: FEB130247
Price: $29.99/$35.00 CAN | Format: TP

ALSO AVAILABLE: LUCIFER BOOKS TWO-FIVE

LUCIFER VOL. 1: COLD HEAVEN

The author of the #1 *New York Times* best-selling novel series *The Spiderwick Chronicles*, Holly Black, makes her Vertigo debut with the continuing tales of the former angel Lucifer.

Writer: Holly Black | Artist: Lee Garbett
ISBN: 978-1-4012-6193-1 | Diamond Code: MAY160345
Price: $14.99/$17.99 CAN | Format: TP

PREACHER BOOK ONE

Jesse Custer, a wayward preacher, begins a violent journey to find God (literally), joined by his girlfriend, Tulip, and the hard-drinking Irish vampire Cassidy.

Writer: Garth Ennis | Artist: Steve Dillon
ISBN: 978-1-4012-4045-5 | Diamond Code: MAR130303
Price: $19.99/$23.99 CAN | Format: TP

ALSO AVAILABLE: PREACHER BOOKS TWO-SIX

PRIDE OF BAGHDAD DELUXE EDITION

Inspired by true events, acclaimed writer Brian K. Vaughan brings readers a startlingly original look at life on the streets of Baghdad during the Iraq War.

Writer: Brian K. Vaughan | Artist: Niko Henrichon
ISBN: 978-1-4012-4894-9 | Diamond Code: AUG140360
Price: $24.99/$28.99 CAN | Format: HC

SAGA OF THE SWAMP THING BOOK ONE

Alan Moore's take on the classic monster stretched the creative boundaries of the medium and became one of the most spectacular series in comic book history.

Writer: Alan Moore | Artist: Stephen Bissette
ISBN: 978-1-4012-2083-9 | Diamond Code: JAN120343
Price: $19.99/$23.99 CAN | Format: TP

ALSO AVAILABLE: SAGA OF THE SWAMP THING BOOKS TWO-SIX

SCALPED VOL. 1: INDIAN COUNTRY

Dashiell Bad Horse must return to the land he grew up on, determined to clean up the crime-ridden "rez" he left years ago, one way or another.

Writer: Jason Aaron | Artist: R.M. Guéra
ISBN: 978-1-4012-1317-6 | Diamond Code: APR108251
Price: $14.99/$17.99 CAN | Format: TP

ALSO AVAILABLE: SCALPED VOL. 2-10

SHERIFF OF BABYLON VOL. 1: BANG. BANG. BANG.

Inspired by his real-life experiences as a CIA operations officer in Iraq, Tom King delivers a wartime crime thriller like no other.

Writer: Tom King | Artist: Mitch Gerads
ISBN: 978-1-4012-6466-6 | Diamond Code: APR160424
Price: $14.99/ $17.99 CAN | Format: TP

TRANSMETROPOLITAN VOL. 1: BACK ON THE STREET

Mastermind writer Warren Ellis delivers this sharp, manic, anything-goes exploration of urban life about journalist/cult author Spider Jerusalem.

Writer: Warren Ellis | Artist: Darick Robertson
ISBN: 978-1-4012-2084-6 | Diamond Code: DEC080220
Price: $14.99/$17.99 CAN | Format: TP

ALSO AVAILABLE: TRANSMETROPOLITAN VOL. 2-10

THE TWILIGHT CHILDREN

Critically acclaimed creators Gilbert Hernandez and Darwyn Cooke team up for this surreal tale in which a sleepy seaside village may be facing an alien invasion.

Writer: Gilbert Hernandez | Artist: Darwyn Cooke
ISBN: 978-1-4012-6245-7 | Diamond Code: FEB160268
Price: $14.99/$17.99 CAN | Format: TP

THE UNWRITTEN VOL. 1: TOMMY TAYLOR AND THE ROGUS IDENTITY

Tom Taylor, the inspiration for the boy wizard from the series of novels his father made famous, finds that the worlds of fiction and real life are crossing into each other in this fantastic graphic novel.

Writer: Mike Carey | Artist: Peter Gross
ISBN: 978-1-4012-2565-0 | Diamond Code: APR128238
Price: $14.99/$17.99 CAN | Format: TP

ALSO AVAILABLE: THE UNWRITTEN VOL. 2-11

Y: THE LAST MAN BOOK ONE

Brian K. Vaughan's epic series that made him a comics legend poses the question "What would you do if you were the last man on Earth?"

Writer: Brian K. Vaughan | Artist: Pia Guerra
ISBN: 978-1-4012-5151-2 | Diamond Code: JUN140312
Price: $19.99/$23.99 CAN | Format: TP

ALSO AVAILABLE: Y: THE LAST MAN BOOKS TWO-FIVE

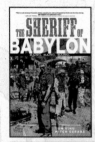

Introducing DC's Young Animal—a four-book grassroots mature-reader imprint, creatively spearheaded by Eisner Award-winning writer and rock icon Gerard Way! This avant-garde imprint bridges the gap between the DCU and Vertigo, focusing on the collision of visual and thematic storytelling. These are comics for dangerous humans.

CAVE CARSON HAS A CYBERNETIC EYE VOL. 1: GOING UNDERGROUND

From deep within the DC mythology, Cave Carson—everyone's favorite spelunker—is back for a whole new adventure as Gerard Way takes readers on an absurd journey through a world that can only be understood when looking through a cybernetic eye.

Writers: Gerard Way & Jon Rivera | Artist: Michael Avon Oeming
ISBN: 978-1-4012-7082-7 | Diamond Code: TK | Price: $16.99/$22.99 CAN
Format: TP | Coming June 20, 2017

DOOM PATROL VOL. 1: BRICK BY BRICK

Grant Morrison's classic misfit team—the Doom Patrol—is reintroduced by Eisner Award-winning writer and rock star Gerard Way in a bombastic new series.

Writer: Gerard Way | Artist: Nick Derington
ISBN: 978-1-4012-6979-1 | Diamond Code: TK
Price: $16.99/$22.99 CAN | Format: TP | Coming June 6, 2017

SHADE, THE CHANGING GIRL VOL. 1: EARTH GIRL MADE EASY

An alien girl from a faraway planet takes up residence in the body of a young Earth girl and chaos ensues in this reimagining of the classic SHADE, THE CHANGING MAN.

Writer: Cecil Castellucci | Artist: Marley Zarcone
ISBN: 978-1-4012-7099-5 | Diamond Code: TK
Price: $16.99/$22.99 | Format: TP | Coming July 4, 2017

MOTHER PANIC VOL. 1: WORK IN PROGRESS

If Batman has taught the world anything, it's that Gotham City needs its vigilantes! Enter Mother Panic! Motivated by her traumatic youth, celebutante Violet Paige seeks to exact vengeance on her privileged peers as she disguises herself as the terrifying new vigilante known only as Mother Panic.

Writers: Jody Houser | Artist: Tommy Lee Edwards
ISBN: 978-1-4012-7111-4 | Diamond Code: TK
Price: $16.99/$22.99 CAN | Format: TP | Coming July 18, 2017

DC's YOUNG ANIMAL

MAD

For over six decades, MAD has been a part of the American humor landscape, for better or worse, but mostly for worse. Armed with irreverence and a sense of duty to satirize and parody anything and everything in pop culture, MAD has been a staple in bedrooms, living rooms, dorm rooms and recycling bins.

GOODNIGHT BATCAVE

Batman just can't seem to get a good night's sleep in this MAD homage to the popular children's book.

Writer: Dave Croatto | Artist: Tom Richmond
ISBN: 978-1-4012-7010-0 | Diamond Code: JUL160389
Price: $14.99/$17.99 CAN | Format: HC

SPY VS. SPY: FIGHT TO THE FINISH

The diabolical duo of double-crosses and deceit (one dressed in black, the other in white) continue to one-up each other until death do they part.

Writer: Peter Kuper | Artist: Peter Kuper
ISBN: 978-1-4012-3527-7 | Diamond Code: AUG118124
Price: $9.99/$11.99 CAN | Format: TP

MAD: SPY VS. SPY SECRET FILES

The adventures of the popular MAD serial by Peter Kuper continue.

Writer: Peter Kuper | Artist: Peter Kuper
ISBN: 978-1-4012-3527-7 | Diamond Code: AUG118124
Price: $9.99/$11.99 CAN | Format: TP

DC Super Hero Girls is a thrilling new universe of super-heroic storytelling that helps build character and confidence, empowering girls to discover their true potential. Developed for girls ages 6-12, DC SUPER HERO GIRLS features DC's most powerful female characters as they make their way through Super Hero High and learn that fun, friendship and hard work are all parts of growing up!

DC SUPER HERO GIRLS: FINALS CRISIS

It's the night before finals and the student body is hard at work...and nothing is going right! The first original graphic novel in the DC Super Hero Girls line is here!

Writer: Shea Fontana | Artist: Yancey Labat
ISBN: 978-1-4012-6247-1 | Diamond Code: APR160322
Price: $9.99/$11.99 CAN | Format: TP

DC SUPER HERO GIRLS: HITS AND MYTHS

As Wonder Woman, Batgirl, Supergirl, Bumblebee, Poison Ivy, Katana and Harley Quinn study Homer's classic epic poem, *The Odyssey*, they find themselves on their own epic journey!

Writer: Shea Fontana | Artist: Yancey Labat
ISBN: 9781401267612 | Diamond Code: AUG160270
Price: $9.99/$13.50 CAN | Format: TP

DC SUPER HERO GIRLS: SUMMER OLYMPUS

School's out for summer, and the girls of Super Hero High are joining Wonder Woman to visit her dad, Zeus. But once among the gods, Wonder Woman faces a huge decision that could change her life forever—and might risk the lives of her friends!

Writer: Shea Fontana | Artist: Yancey Labat
ISBN: 9781401272357 | Price: $9.99/$13.50 CAN
Format: TP | Coming July 11, 2017

COLLECTIBLES

DC Collectibles produces an exclusive line of high-quality products, bringing to life stories and characters from DC's wide range of world-renowned characters. Ranging from action figures to statues and unique entertainment properties such as DC Bombshells to *Batman: The Animated Series*, these products are among the finest available in the collectible realm.

DC ICONS

Taken from their most popular stories and well-renowned designs, DC's superheroes and villains are immortalized here in this amazing line of detailed action figures.

BATMAN
(LAST RITES)
ACTION
FIGURE

Diamond Code:
MAY150286
Price: $28.00

SUPERMAN
(MAN OF STEEL)
ACTION FIGURE

Diamond Code:
AUG150313
Price: $28.00

THE FLASH
(CHAIN
LIGHTNING)
ACTION FIGURE

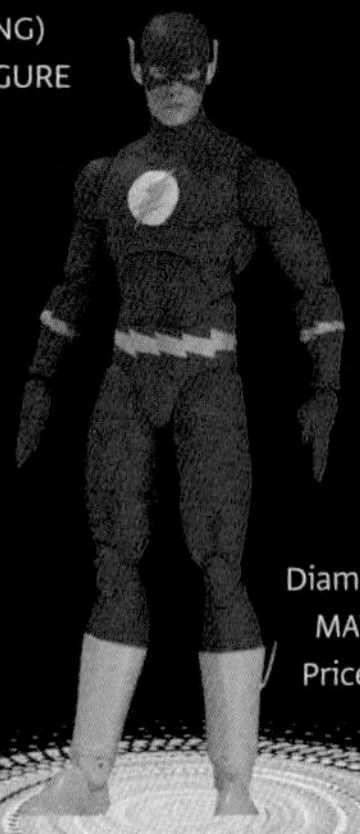

Diamond Code:
MAY150295
Price: $28.00

BATGIRL AND MOTORCYCLE
(BATGIRL OF BURNSIDE)
DELUXE ACTION FIGURE

Diamond Code:
MAY160364
Price: $60.00

HARLEY QUINN
(NO MAN'S LAND)
ACTION FIGURE

Diamond Code:
AUG150314
Price: $28.00

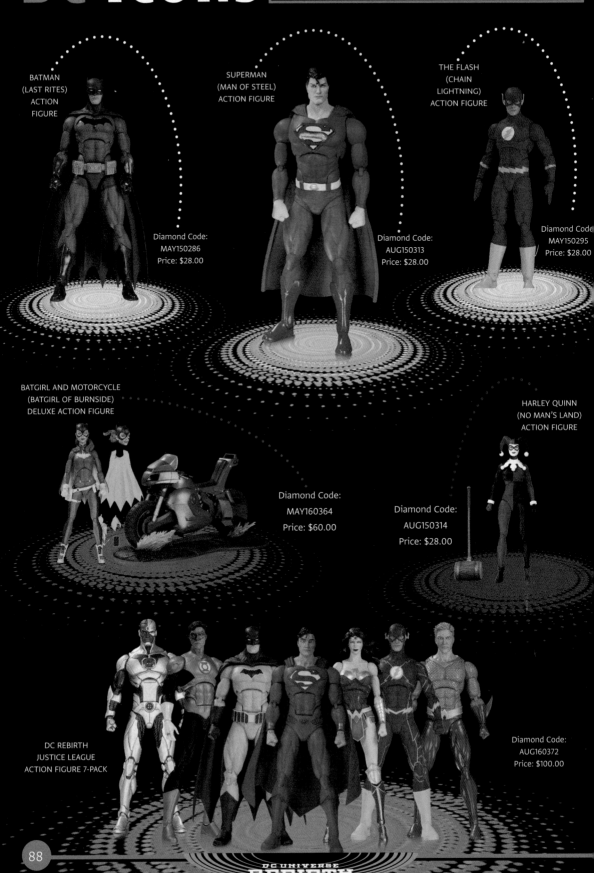

DC REBIRTH
JUSTICE LEAGUE
ACTION FIGURE 7-PACK

Diamond Code:
AUG160372
Price: $100.00

As Word War II rages across Europe, the Allied forces issue a call to arms for the greatest heroines the world has ever known: THE BOMBSHELLS! This original DC Collectibles franchise takes comics most popular heroines and reimagines them in the 1940s.

DC COMICS Bombshells

BATWOMAN STATUE
Diamond Code: MAR150325
Price: $125.00

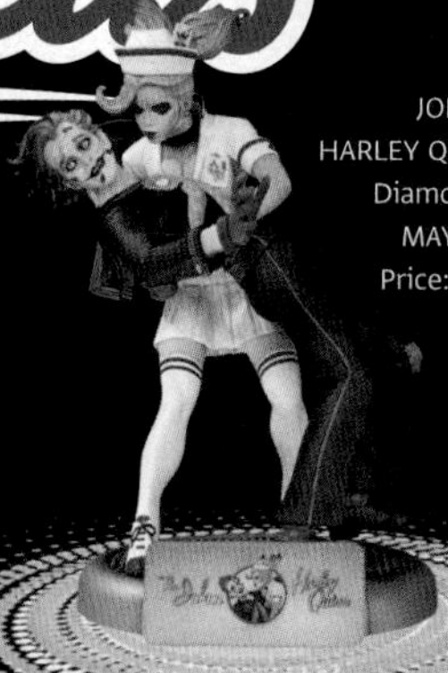

JOKER & HARLEY QUINN STATUE
Diamond Code: MAY150291
Price: $250.00

HOLIDAY WONDER WOMAN STATUE
Diamond Code: MAY150292 | Price: $125.00

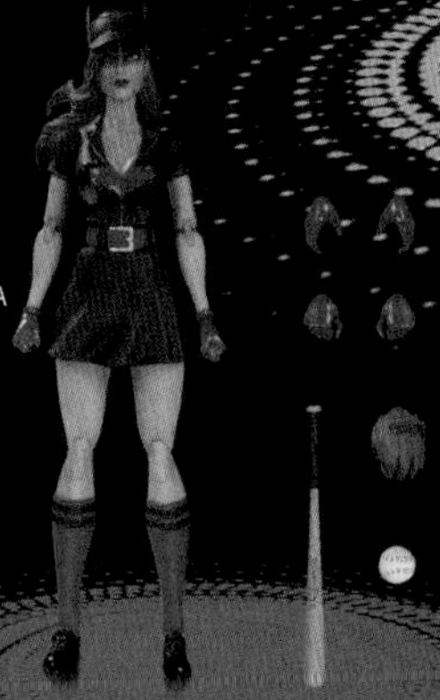

DC DESIGNER SERIES ANT LUCIA BOMBSHELLS BATWOMAN ACTION FIGURE
Diamond Code: JUN168021
Price: $28.00

DC DESIGNER SERIES ANT LUCIA BOMBSHELLS HARLEY QUINN ACTION FIGURE
Diamond Code: JUN168019
Price: $28.00

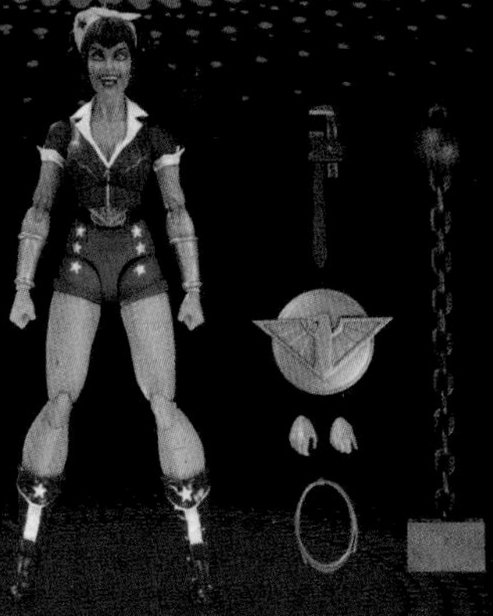

DC DESIGNER SERIES ANT LUCIA BOMBSHELLS WONDER WOMAN ACTION FIGURE
Diamond Code: JUN168021
Price: $28.00

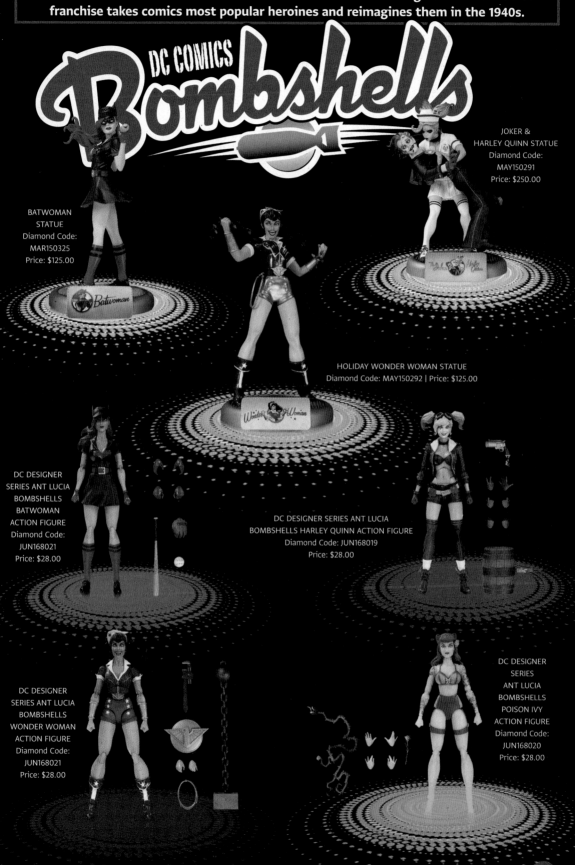

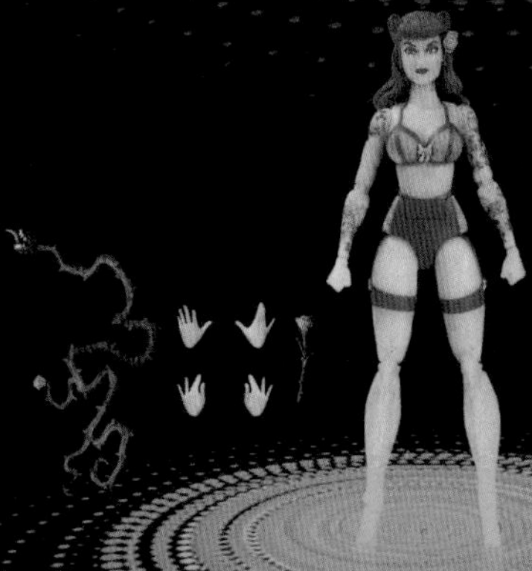

DC DESIGNER SERIES ANT LUCIA BOMBSHELLS POISON IVY ACTION FIGURE
Diamond Code: JUN168020
Price: $28.00

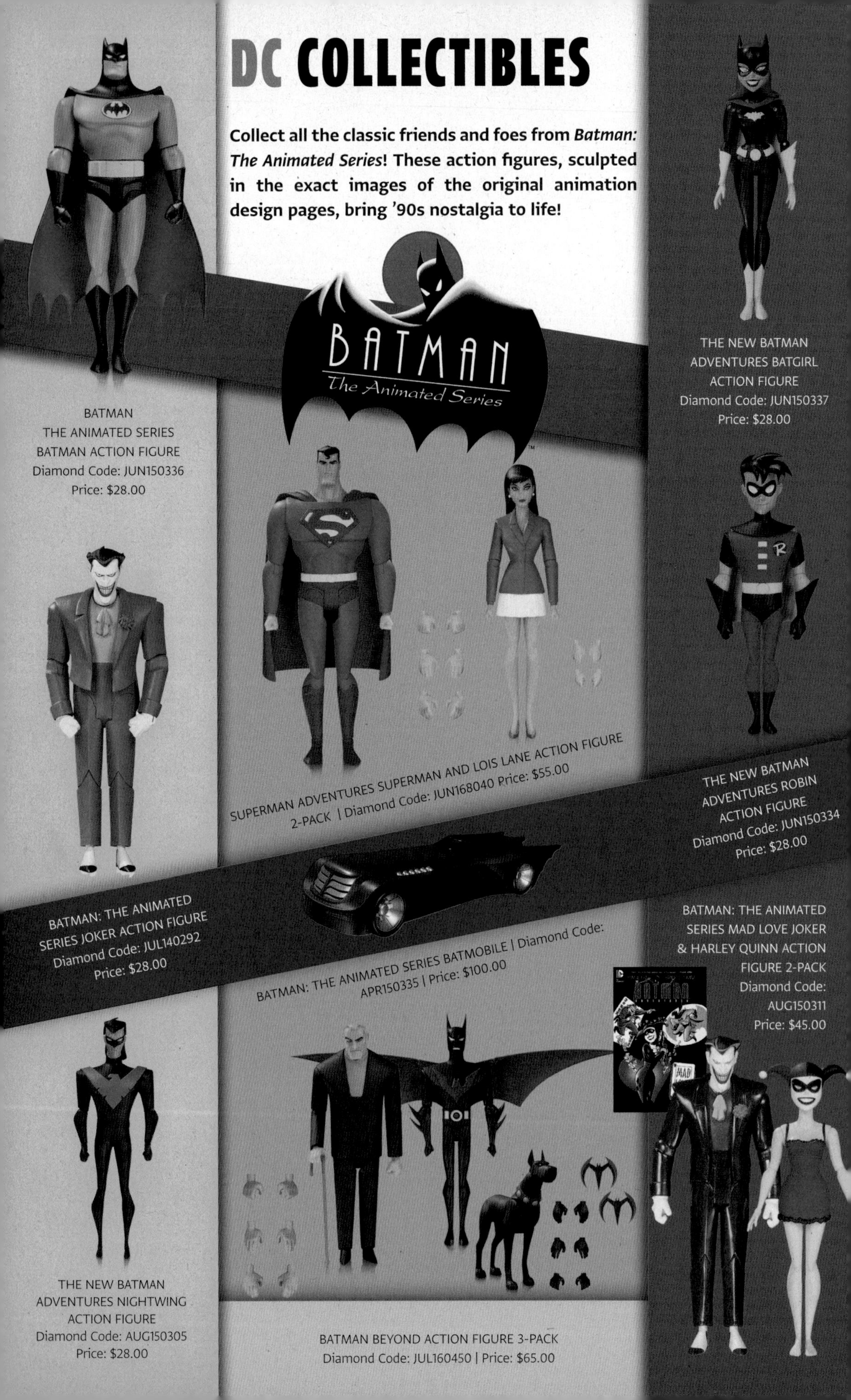
DC COLLECTIBLES
Collect all the classic friends and foes from Batman: The Animated Series! These action figures, sculpted in the exact images of the original animation design pages, bring '90s nostalgia to life!
BATMAN The Animated Series
BATMAN THE ANIMATED SERIES BATMAN ACTION FIGURE Diamond Code: JUN150336 Price: $28.00
THE NEW BATMAN ADVENTURES BATGIRL ACTION FIGURE Diamond Code: JUN150337 Price: $28.00
SUPERMAN ADVENTURES SUPERMAN AND LOIS LANE ACTION FIGURE 2-PACK | Diamond Code: JUN168040 Price: $55.00
THE NEW BATMAN ADVENTURES ROBIN ACTION FIGURE Diamond Code: JUN150334 Price: $28.00
BATMAN: THE ANIMATED SERIES JOKER ACTION FIGURE Diamond Code: JUL140292 Price: $28.00
BATMAN: THE ANIMATED SERIES BATMOBILE | Diamond Code: APR150335 | Price: $100.00
BATMAN: THE ANIMATED SERIES MAD LOVE JOKER & HARLEY QUINN ACTION FIGURE 2-PACK Diamond Code: AUG150311 Price: $45.00
THE NEW BATMAN ADVENTURES NIGHTWING ACTION FIGURE Diamond Code: AUG150305 Price: $28.00
BATMAN BEYOND ACTION FIGURE 3-PACK Diamond Code: JUL160450 | Price: $65.00

DC DESIGNER SERIES

For decades, DC has been home to some of the most visionary artists in all of comics. Now these classic interpretations of your favorite characters have been immortalized in action figure form with these Designer Series action figures.

DESIGNER SERIES AMANDA CONNER
SUPERHERO HARLEY QUINN
ACTION FIGURE
Diamond Code: APR160441 | Price: $28.00

DESIGNER SERIES AMANDA CONNER
HOLIDAY HARLEY QUINN ACTION FIGURE
Diamond Code: APR160439
Price: $28.00

DESIGNER SERIES AMANDA CONNER
TRADITIONAL HARLEY QUINN
ACTION FIGURE
Diamond Code: APR160442 Price: $28.00

DESIGNER SERIES AMANDA CONNER
SPACESUIT HARLEY QUINN ACTION FIGURE
Diamond Code: APR160440 Price: $28.00

DESIGNER SERIES GREG CAPULLO BATMAN ACTION FIGURE
Diamond Code: NOV130284 | Price: $28.00

Capullo

DESIGNER SERIES GREG CAPULLO NIGHTWING ACTION FIGURE
Diamond Code: NOV130286 | Price: $28.00

DARWYN COOKE

DESIGNER SERIES DARWYN COOKE BATMAN ACTION FIGURE
Diamond Code: DEC150380
Price: $28.00

DESIGNER SERIES DARWYN COOKE HARLEY QUINN
ACTION FIGURE
Diamond Code: DEC150381
Price: $28.00

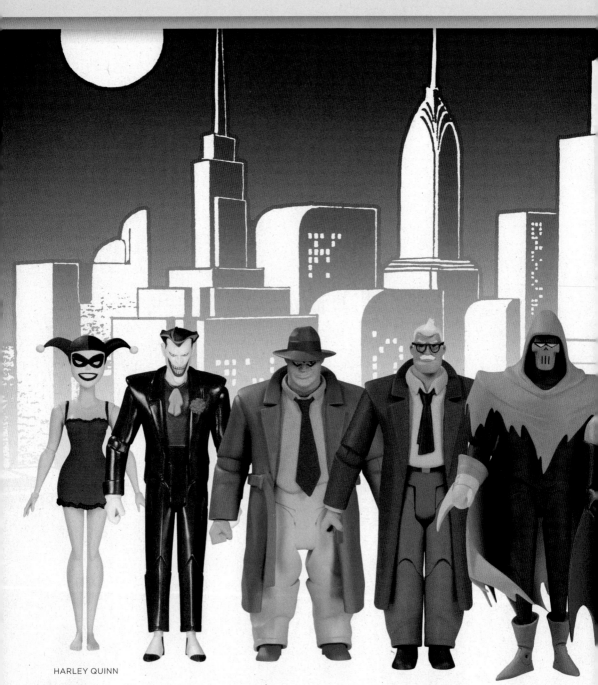

)-WINNING
E!
BATMAN
The Animated Series
ACTION FIGURES
BATMAN
RA'S AL GHUL
ZATANNA
VENTRILOQUIST & SCARFACE
TALIA AL GHUL
THE JOKER
NEAR YOU. COLLECT THEM ALL!
BATMAN and all related characters and elements © & ™ DC Comics and Warner Bros. Entertainment Inc. (s16)

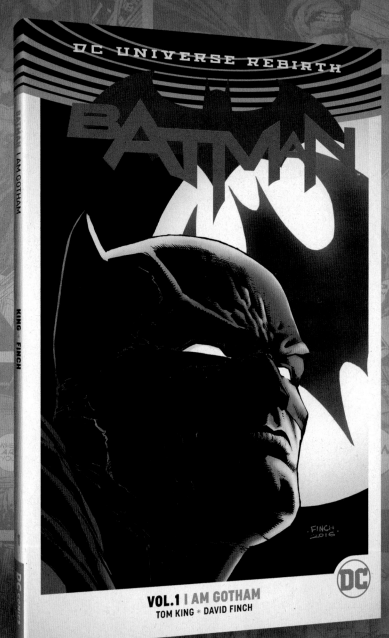

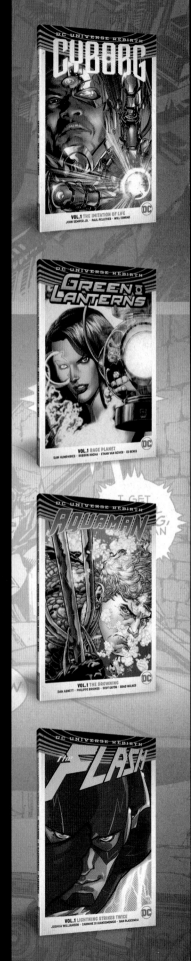

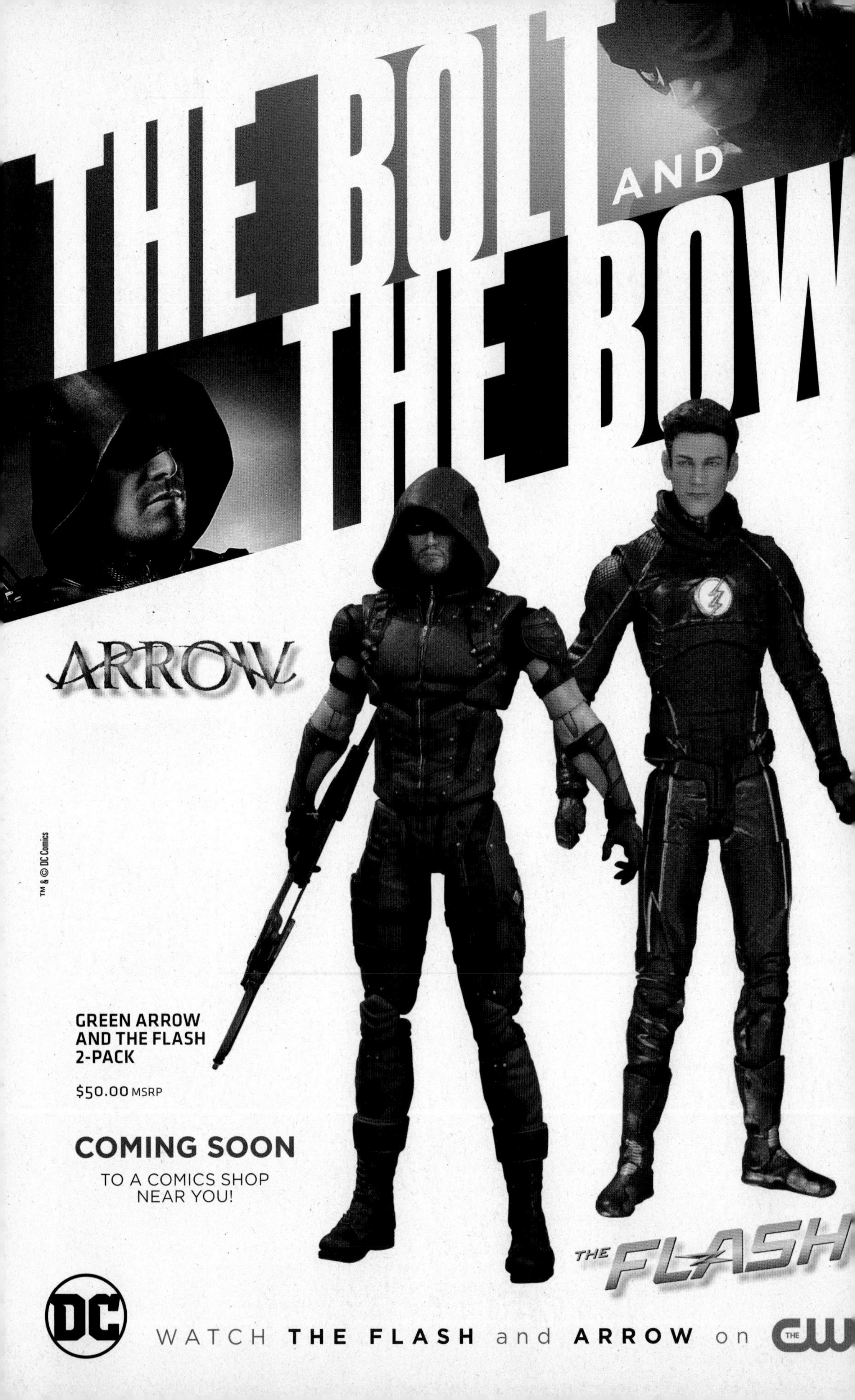
THE BOLT AND THE BOW
ARROW
GREEN ARROW AND THE FLASH 2-PACK
$50.00 MSRP
COMING SOON
TO A COMICS SHOP NEAR YOU!
TM & © DC Comics
THE FLASH
DC
WATCH THE FLASH and ARROW on THE CW